In August of 2003, a [ ] *collaboration of America* ... *Romanian military troops conducted an expedition beneath the Romanian Sphinx in the Bucegi Mountains and uncovered the greatest archeological find of all time: a mysterious chamber some 50,000 years old with holographic technology that is beyond man's wildest dreams.*

Despite the political intrigue, turmoil and restriction around this great discovery, the leader of the expedition enabled Radu Cinamar to visit and explore these artifacts. Ever since, Radu's life has been a labyrinthine adventure of strange events, clandestine liaisons and extraordinary people and circumstances.

Transylvanian Moonrise tells the story of Radu's meeting with a Tibetan lama which is arranged by a mysterious alchemist whose ancestors have lived for hundreds of years by pursuing a secret tradition of the Great Work which prolongs life indefinitely until one can evolve beyond the physical plane. When Radu's meeting takes place, the lama is accompanied by a yidam, a mysterious creature with supernatural powers that is created through a ritual using a Tibetan sand mandala. The lama reveals how he set the aforementioned events in motion in order to fix major imbalances in the Earth.

Transylvanian Moonrise: A Secret Initiation in the Mysterious Land of the Gods is not only a remarkable story, but it is an initiation of the highest order that will take you far beyond your ordinary imagination in order to describe events that have molded the past and will influence the future in the decades ahead.

✹

TRANSYLVANIAN MOONRISE
A SECRET INITIATION IN THE
MYSTERIOUS LAND OF THE GODS

BY RADU CINAMAR

INTRODUCTION, EDITING & PART II
BY PETER MOON

NEW YORK

Transylvanian Moonrise: A Secret Initiation in the Mysterious Land of the Gods
Originally published in the Romanian language as
Twelve Days: A Secret Initiation in the Mysterious Land of the Gods
Copyright (Part 1) © 2006 by Radu Cinamar
Copyright (Part 2) © 2011 by Peter Moon
First English language printing, May 2011
International copyright laws apply

Cover art by April Pinsonneault
Typography by Creative Circle Inc.
Published by: Sky Books
        Box 769
        Westbury, New York 11590
        email: *skybooks@yahoo.com*
        website: www.skybooksusa.com
              www.digitalmontauk.com

Library of Congress Cataloging-in-Publication Data

Cinamar, Radu / Moon, Peter
        Transylvanian Moonrise
by Radu Cinamar with Peter Moon
        288 pages
        ISBN 978-0-9678162-8-9
1. Body, Mind, Spirit: Occultism 2. Body, Mind, Spirit: General
Library of Congress Control Number 2010943365

This book is dedicated to Machandi

OTHER TITLES FROM SKY BOOKS

by Preston Nichols and Peter Moon
The Montauk Project: Experiments in Time
Montauk Revisited: Adventures in Synchronicity
Pyramids of Montauk: Explorations in Consciousness
Encounter in the Pleiades: An Inside Look at UFOs
The Music of Time

by Peter Moon
The Black Sun: Montauk's Nazi-Tibetan Connection
Synchronicity and the Seventh Seal
The Montauk Book of the Dead
The Montauk Book of the Living
Spandau Mystery

by Joseph Matheny with Peter Moon
Ong's Hat: The Beginning

by Stewart Swerdlow
Montauk: The Alien Connection
The Healer's Handbook: A Journey Into Hyperspace

by Alexandra Bruce
The Philadelphia Experiment Murder:
Parallel Universes and the Physics of Insanity

by Wade Gordon
The Brookhaven Connection

by Radu Cinamar with Peter Moon
Tranyslvanian Sunrise

CONTENTS

LEFT PROFILE OF THE ROMANIAN SPHINX
This is the sphinx beneath which, according to Radu Cinamar, there is a chamber built some 50,000 years ago which contains technology that is far more advanced that our current human technology.

RIGHT PROFILE OF THE ROMANIAN SPHINX
This is the same rock as the above sphinx but the photograph is from the other side. Behind the "cat's whiskers" is the shape of a woman with long hair which is more pronounced in color. It is not graffiti but seems to be crafted by nature. There are many rock formations in this part of the world that appear to have been designed by superior beings who utilized the elements of nature to create mysterious art work.

INTRODUCTION

In 2009 we published *Transylvanian Sunrise* which told the story of a remarkable discovery beneath the Romanian Sphinx in the Bucegi Mountains of Romania. It all began when Radu Cinamar, the author, was invited to meet a very mysterious man who worked in the most secretive department of Romania's intelligence service. His name is Cezar Brad.

Cezar came to the attention of the Romanian secret service on the day he was born. The doctor was not able to cut his incredibly thick umbilical cord and duly reported this, as he would any other anomaly, to the communist authorities. Cezar's parents were then visited by state security and a financial arrangement was made whereby they would report any unusual behavior emanating from or associated with the child. As Cezar began to demonstrate extra sensitive or psychic behavior, he was brought under the tutelage of a mysterious Dr. Xien, on loan to Romania from Red China as part of a cultural exchange program between the two communist countries.

Cezar's tutoring came under the jurisdiction of Department Zero, the most secretive apparatus in Romania's intelligence service. It was also referred to as the Occult Department and literally became Cezar's home after the age of twelve. He would eventually grow up to become the head of this department and answered only to a mysterious General Obadea who answered directly to the Communist Dictator. With an uncanny amount of tact, both Cezar and General Obadea held their positions in Department Zero after the fall of the dictator Ceauşescu.

It was while running the "X Files" department of the Romanian government that Cezar was approached by a man who would change the destiny of Romania forever. This was Signore Massini, one of the highest ranking members of Italian Freemasonry who also claimed to be a high ranking member of the Bilderbergers. Massini explained that the satellite radar technology of the Pentagon revealed that there was a hidden chamber beneath the Romanian Sphinx. He offered Cezar, who had considerable autonomy when it came to conducting secret investigations, many false promises if he would cooperate in letting his people excavate in order to reach this chamber.

Although he did not trust Massini one bit, Cezar knew that if he resisted his request he would soon be replaced in Department Zero. As the Romanian President and the head of security were the only ones outside of Department Zero to know of its existence, Cezar realized that Massini must have very special connections indeed for him to even know who Cezar was. Accordingly, he felt the smartest thing to do was to play along.

Eventually, through its strange affiliation with Italian Free-masonry, the Pentagon sent in American troops to do the tunneling and excavation required to access the hidden chamber. It took high powered atomic laser technology to get the job done and there were many difficulties. After many trials and tribulations, success was achieved. The hidden chamber was unsealed and it revealed far more than one might ever imagine. This included technology whereby one could place their hand on a table and see their own DNA in microscopic form in three-dimensional holograms. Other devices on the table enabled one to see the DNA of alien species from other planets with accompanying star renderings so that one could see where they actually came from. By placing two hands on different parts of the table, one could also "mix" the DNA of two species so as to see how they might look if hybridized. As the tables themselves were six feet high, it seemed the creatures who built them, perhaps 50,000 years ago, were gigantic compared to humans of today.

This remarkable chamber also included a "Projection Hall" whereby one could see a holographic rendition of the history of

Earth that was tailored to the individuality of whoever might be viewing it. This history, however, abruptly cuts off in about the Fifth Century A.D., perhaps because it required some sort of software update. One of the more intriguing aspects of the Projection Hall is that it also contains three mysterious tunnels that lead into the bowels of the Earth and similar facilitates in Iraq, Mongolia, Tibet and also beneath the Giza Plateau in Egypt. One of the tunnels leads, quite enigmatically, into the Inner Earth itself.

Although this was the most remarkable discovery ever made in the history of archeology, the politics around the situation became highly strained with the Romanians, the Americans and the Italian Freemasonry all vying for control. Despite the extreme political tension, Cezar Brad arranged for Radu Cinamar to visit the hidden chamber and the projection hall itself. His account is given in *Transylvanian Sunrise*, the predecessor to this book.

Political tensions reach a climax which is triggered by American soldiers who are guarding a similar chamber with holographic technology that was previously discovered near Baghdad. As they watch over this other mysterious chamber, they witness a holographic projection showing them that a similar device in Romania has been discovered. Their report to their superiors through standard command channels results in a rather furious investigation which eventually reveals that the Pentagon has forces in Romania. Ultimately, the American president calls the Romanian president in an effort to find out what is going on. The Italian Freemason is forced to abandon the scene for his own self-preservation and what ensues in the end, after many heated negotiations, is unprecedented diplomatic relations between Romania and the United States. Romania becomes a part of NATO.

While the claims made my Radu Cinamar are extraordinary, so are the circumstances surrounding them. Many of these are verifiable and you will read about them in this book. As of this writing, I have visited Romania for three consecutive years (2008-2010) and have had occasion to see some very interesting parts of that country, including the sphinx. After meeting with many different Romanians and also receiving many communications from Radu, it is my privileged and learned opinion that the events he describes are genuine. The story you are about to read is even more remarkable than what was presented in the first book. It also corrects the only major flaw in that original manuscript because it elucidates and develops the most intriguing character therein. I am referring to the mysterious and enigmatic Dr. Xien who oversaw the education and psychic development of Cezar Brad, all the time priming him to become the head of Department Zero. As the story developed, Dr. Xien disappeared and we never heard what happened to him nor did we find out who he really was. As you will soon read, Dr. Xien was part of the Chinese government's special "psychic team," but he was actually an incognito Tibetan lama with an agenda all his own.

Transylvanian Sunrise and *Transylvanian Moonrise* are books that will cause you to stretch your boundaries of what is possible. This is not a bad thing. Stretching your muscles makes them more pliable and flexible in dealing with the obstacles that life can throw at you. You are hereby invited to stretch your mind. A flexible mind will enable you to better cope with the challenges you might encounter in your own life.

In Part II of this book, I have reported on additional developments as well as my own adventures in Tranyslvania. This is an ongoing drama that is expected to continue for many years to come.

PETER MOON

EDITOR'S NOTE

Note: *The following Editor's Note is from Sorin Hurmuz, the editor and publisher of Radu Cinamar's original book which is entitled* Viitor cu cap de mort *in the Romanian language. This translates as* Death's Head Future *in English, however, the name of* Transylvanian Sunrise *has been chosen for the English language version.* Viitor cu cap de mort *and* Transylvanian Sunrise *are one and the same book.*

The publishing of *Viitor cu cap de mort* forced society to confront a disturbing reality. Indeed, we can say that the work of Radu Cinamar generated many question marks within people's consciousness. Some readers tried to find out the hidden meaning behind his incredible narrative. A central newspaper dedicated two pages to this subject, partially confirming various elements in the book. We want to thank all those who shared their discoveries with us as well as those who sent positive feedback.

During the time that has passed since publishing *Transylvanian Sunrise*, our editorial staff received numerous calls from readers expressing their opinion over the very exciting subject of the book. Most readers had a very favorable reaction and congratulated us for having the courage to publish such a book. Besides the great discovery in the Bucegi Mountains, which is described in the last chapter of the book, it is also important to point out that Radu Cinamar offered us a true gold mine of esoteric information that can guide us in our everyday life. These very important elements are delivered by the author in such a direct and categorical way and had such an impact over the readers that we happily see the book becoming a best-seller in its category.

I have often been asked if I know the author personally and if what is written in the book is true. As I have already alluded to, there are numerous confirmations related to what is written in *Transylvanian Sunrise*. One surprising proof was included in an article signed by Adina Mutar in the February 7, 2005 edition of *Ziarul* newspaper out of which I have selected a few fragments:

"Cabinet 1 set up a special unit to study paranormal phenomena and to train 'para soldiers' in the Buzau Mountains. Cabinet 2 was envious. This is how a unit of 'paranormals' was formed at the orders of Elena Ceauşescu, a unit that received diverse missions from her, including searching for treasures of legend. First of all, Elena's men were there to spy on the 'para soldiers' led by General Ilie Ceauşescu. Then, after obtaining certain 'abilities,' Elena's men were sent to look for ancient treasures hidden in mysterious caves in the Carpathians, particularly in Bucegi, were it was said that an immense gallery exists that is filled with gold."

NATIONAL SECURITY'S DEPARTMENT ZERO

"At the end of last year, a strange book entitled *Transylvanian Sunrise* by Radu Cinamar was published. It mentions some sensational discoveries by Department Zero, a secret department of State Security with many zeros, which means it was very secret. It was founded in 1968 at the orders of Nicolae Ceauşescu to discover, educate and develop human subjects with unusual capacities based upon the models of the USA, USSR and China, countries who are very advanced in that field. As Ceauşescu was not on good terms with the Russians at that time and refused to support Moscow in what was called the Prague Spring, it seems, according to the author of the book, that a treaty was signed with

China which specified that a certain Dr. Xien, a master of parapsychology, would organize and supervise the activity of this ultra secret department for fifteen years while Romania offered study grants to one hundred Chinese students during the same period. The author placed the location of two of Department Zero's bases with one being 'close to town B' and another one in the Retezat Mountains. He also mentions a few significant missions named 'K events' such as the disappearance of people from the Buzau Mountains in 1981 that we covered as well in a past edition of *Ziarul*. We are also told about a detection system of 'the specific frequency of vibration of every being, object or phenomena based on the principle of resonance.' This is actually a machine invented by Carol Przybilla and under the absolute 'protection' of Elena Ceauşescu's 'security.'"

MEN IN BLACK IN BOZIORU

"Starting from an evidentiary data base that was revealed by others who were involved at that time in such activities, we discover that the 'K events' of the mysterious Department Zero merge with those of the paranormal army unit, based in the Bucegi Mountains, that were subordinate to General Ilie Ceauşescu. Researcher Vasile Rudan, a specialist in extrasensory perceptions, worked for this unit under a strict contract. He led extrasensory experiments on gifted children and all the reports, photos, negatives, and film strips were handed over to the respective unit. He was not allowed to keep anything. [...]"

CABINET 2 IS SPYING

"I contacted General Nicolae Plesita and asked him

about Security's Department Zero and its paranormal preoccupations.

'I've never heard of such a thing,' he said. 'I heard about the Army ones but not the Security ones. But Elena Ceauşescu was dealing with such issues within the National Council of Technology and Science over which she presided. The first vice-president was Ion Ursu. Within the NCTS was a department that had in their responsibilities any research or experimentation of such phenomena. [...]

'After further "digging," I have found out from a retired colonel who used to work in DNS (Department of National Security) that indeed there were people within the NCTS who had the job description "monitoring paranormal research," their reports being under Code Zero and sent to Elena Ceauşescu. She distributed it to three subordinates. Two of these would be working for the DNS. One would get the reports about strategic deposits – uranium, petrol – that were discovered by extrasensory perceptions, while the other would get certain inventions, further on dealt with by the Institute of Advanced Technology. The third one was in charge of the issues of Elena Ceauşescu's personal interest. In other words, Ceauşescu's paranormals were doing all the work and those from Cabinet 2 were spying on them and stealing their reports. [...]' "

THE LEGENDS OF PELES

"Elena Ceauşescu found out about the treasures in Bucegi thanks to queen Elisabeta-Carmen Sylca who, in the book *Stories of Peles* gathered many stories from locals and shepherds about the fabulous treasures that were hidden deep in the mountains. It is written that in 'the Hag's Castle' there is a subterranean fortress where an enormous amount of gold is deposited. It seems like it was not by chance that king Carol I picked this place to build Peles castle – inaugurated in 1883 – in Bucegi. Many foreign publications have observed the strange ensemble of megalithic sculptures on the Sphinx-Babele slope and the caves guarded by monasteries. The priests, keepers and guardians of secret treasures left by our ancestors from generation to generation, had built a true network of monasteries as a first line of defense and fortification. [...]"

THE SACRED CAVE IN BUCEGI

"First of all, the publications writing about caves or treasures were monitored. In the study named 'Hyperborean Dacia,' published in Paris in 1936 and then republished in France and Italy in the 1980s when it created a stir, Vasile Lovinescu wrote in these studies that 'Om Mountain (also known as Mount Omu) is traversed by an enormous cave, one of the largest in the world – and its end was never reached – only being explored for approximately 20 km. Who explored it and for what purpose was not mentioned. Between 1966 and 1968, the Peruvian architect Daniel Ruzo came to Romania to examine the sphinx (with whose name he did not agree) which he had seen on a postal card. He was accompanied by a team of Romanians

17

who used this opportunity to film a documentary for the Alexandru Sahia Studios called 'Stone Mysteries.' Ruzo had noticed that the sphinx looked like the main face of an ensemble of statues sculpted on a slope of the Marcahuasi plateau in Peru and named 'The Monument of Mankind.' As a matter of fact, the sphinx is not just a face and is surrounded by other human faces of different races and even the head of a dog. Backing his conclusions on his vast experience, Ruzo says that the dog plays the role of a treasure guardian and that 'there must also be a treasure cave' near this magnificent Monument of Man."

ON THE BRINK OF IMMORTALITY

"Another researcher who made an ample study of the Bucegi summit – a study that reached the offices of Cabinet 2 – was Cristina Panculescu. According to her theory, explored at length in the book *UFO – Parallel Universes* by Colonel Emil Strainu, in Bucegi near Mount Omu there is an energetic-informational center of Terra, pointed to by all the traditions of ancient civilizations. Cristina Panculescu highlighted, through a series of rock sample analysis and electronography, some very special properties of this Sky Pillar – Tree of Life, identified as Ocolit Peak. Finally she proved that the center is a geometric place of cosmic connection, an exit gate out of the terrestrial universe with a measurable energetic activity, manifested in cycles. She observes that since 1986 the intensity of the center went above the latency threshold. The center was also known during the Dacic rule, being placed on the holy mountain Kogayon. 'Called by the sphinx, Dacia's people knew how to become immortal' is the conclusion of the study, finished in 1988 and presented to the

18

Central Committee of the Romanian Communist Party and from there, by mysterious ways, found its way to the desk of Elena Ceauşescu's people. And maybe she too flirted with the idea of immortality as many other leaders throughout history have done with their cohorts of alchemists who sought the Philosophical Stone in order to obtain the elixir of life and turn any metal into gold. Elena Ceauşescu was a 'collector' of all sorts of rejuvenating and recovering practices, be it at home or abroad; but the events of December '89 (meaning revolution) were close and there was no time for other underground exploration except the underground of power. In her time these theories were studied more assiduously although in great secrecy. Today they are made public but the authorities do not seem to care much. As for the fabulous treasure from the Bucegi Mountains, it has not been found simply because the Treasure Gate has not been found and this gate leads to the great gallery that is chock full of gold. It is said, however, in *Transylvanian Sunrise* that this great gallery has been found by NASA satellites and therein lies a priceless treasure with regard to the history of Mankind. But maybe the author rushed things a little bit. [...]"

THE TREASURE GATE

"Elena Ceauşescu's people were well oriented. One of the most fervent researchers of Romania's sacred geography, Dan Corneliu Braneanu, who published numerous articles about the sacerdotal (sacerdotal means priestly) center in Bucegi, confirms that in the depth of the mountain is a network of underground galleries that might connect to several caves that also connect with other sacred centers in the world. He also studied Daniel Ruzo's book *La historia fantastica de un*

19

descubrimiento, published by Diana publishing house in Mexico, about his travels through 'the holy mountains' of Romania that still hold memories of the civilization before the Flood. Ruzo was fascinated by the numerous sacred representations on the cliffs that guard the way to Omu, 'ancient sculptures, made before the Flood, eroded by age' portraying priests and lions, keepers of the treasures. 'I studied many proto historic sacred centers around the world, but here in the Carpathians, I found the Treasure Gate,' wrote Daniel Ruzo. What treasure is he talking about? The answer comes from Dan Corneliu Bradeanu: 'It is not just a material treasure but a mainly spiritual one that transmits information from one cycle to another of civilizations roaming Terra since time immemorial. Lobsang Rampa launched the idea of an underground initiatory deposit in the mountains of Tibet, von Danniken located one in the mountains of Ecuador and Daniel Ruzo felt that the sacred triad ends in Bucegi, if not actually starting here. As for the word OM, it has an important spiritual meaning and that is found in many toponyms only in our country.'"

AT THE THUNDERSTRUCK ROCK

"After much research which also included dowsing or radiesthesy (radionics in English), Corneliu Braneanu assumes that an entrance gate to the underground network beneath Omu could be in the Obarsia Ialomitei Valley in a place dominated by a cliff called 'The Thunderstruck church' or 'The Thunderstruck Rock,' a cliff that ends suddenly in a vertical stone wall that also acts as a supporting wall. At the base of this stone wall you can find shattered stones, probably as a result of an entrance tunnel dug into the subterranean tunnel network (that joins together several caves in Bucegi) excavated over 40.000 years ago (the dating was made by radiesthesy) and which is now covered. The stone figures noticed by Ruzo during his climb towards Omu could mark the vertical plane in which this gate is located, at an actual depth of 12 metres.' "

The excerpts you have just read are not the only corroborations of Radu Cinamar's story. There are others.

I am using this opportunity to inform all of our readers that I personally do not know Mister Radu Cinamar. I have no data, information or references about him and all of my attempts in this direction yielded no result. The content of the book was received by email and all other arrangements were made in the same way, all at the express request of the author. After a few hesitations on my part, mainly due to this unusual way of collaboration, I accepted to publish the material as I considered its exceptional valuable for the Romanian people.

The same procedures were followed with this book you are about to read, a work which you will soon see is even more outrageous than the previous one. Mister Radu Cinamar is a very secretive man and I understand his reasons perfectly, reasons that stem directly from the elements he presents in his books. Nonetheless, I nurture a strong hope that I will get to meet him in a not too distant future, and I have no doubt that this is what the majority of his readers wish for as well.

Transylvanian Moonrise: A Secret Initiation in the Mysterious Land of the Gods manages to turn inside out almost all of our ideas about life and the universe we live in. Although clearly presented, the notions and events in the book can shock our mentality so much that I feel obliged to accept that maybe we all need a profound re-evaluation of the way we think and live.

THE EDITOR (of the original Romanian version)
(SORIN HURMUZ)

BABELE

This rock formation is known as Babele which means "old women" in Romanian, but it also means "gateway" as in the word *Babalon* or *Babylon*. The rock is within a hundred yards of the Romanian Sphinx. The mystery chamber is midway beneath the two monuments but submerged deep within the mountain and far below the surface. If you seek out the military installation nearby, you will be chased away by soldiers before you even get to a fence. There are, however, plenty of hiking trails that are unrestricted and some of these, so it is said, will rejuvenate your energy so that you are not tired after walking for eight hours.

FOREWORD

If the amazing events I was involved in during the past two years had been limited to the extraordinary discovery from the Bucegi Mountains (which I presented in my previous book, *Transylvanian Sunrise*), maybe I would not have had any good reasons to write a new book. Not even the Great Expedition, led by Cezar through the enormous enigmatic underground tunnels starting from the Projection Room, would have had a strong enough impulse upon me to write about its main aspects. There are two reasons why. On the one hand, this is presently one of the greatest state secrets in Romania. Upon his return and just as I expected, Cezar kept his promise of sharing with me the most important events and discoveries of the expedition that he ventured into with an elite commando unit formed by fifteen top-trained army people. Their mission may be the most adventurous and fascinating exploration in the history of Humankind.

Although I do not know every detail of it, I can say that I have a pertinent general perspective of its amazing realities which I learned from Cezar when I met with him at the end of October (2004), a year after he started the expedition. The political climate was quite 'hot' then as we were in that critical time just before the elections. As far as I understood, Cezar's report lasted for five days and he was audited by a special Romanian-American commission. It is even plausible that certain political factors were radically influenced by the new discoveries and evidence that was brought up. I have heard that the members of the auditing committee were so troubled by the data and evidence presented that they were unable to make any decision for several hours or to correctly transmit the information to the top echelon of the state. Their entire system of values was completely turned on its head and there were no other arguments left to support their old beliefs. Maybe that is why it was concluded that a radical transformation of the occult system and influences within the country was necessary.

It is amazing how the chain of events starting with the great discovery in the Bucegi mountains and continuing with the major expedition along the underground tunnels has changed almost for good the way of thinking as well as the destiny of certain people. I count myself among these as I had to rapidly adapt to significant changes in my own existence. These transformations mainly involved my inner being. The occult universe in which I have been gradually initiated by Cezar plus the fact that I am now convinced of certain astounding aspects of the physical and subtle processes of life has encouraged me to spend time studying books and papers on the subject with great interest, thus increasing my knowledge of these aspects which are most often completely ignored by the majority of people.

I have noticed, however, that it is incredibly difficult to depict in a credible way certain situations and events which are on the borderline of the absurd to an ordinary mentality. This is the other reason why I am not going to describe the Great Expedition. Besides the fact that Cezar does not agree with me writing about it, I also think that it is highly unlikely that the account of the unusual trip will have a real impact in the consciousness of most people. Of course, this might only be a transient situation as the way events play themselves out at a global level, especially now in this critical period of Mankind's history, are unpredictable and often shocking. This can cause a once played-down event to be reconsidered at its real value later on. With close analysis, we can see that all that happens in this world follows a guided path whose shining light is already seen by certain human beings who are capable of recognizing it among many other possibilities. We can then expect a rapid and astonishing transformation in people's consciousness; and only then will the elements of the Great

Expedition which started in the Bucegi Mountains be appreciated and understood at their just value. This is the situation with regard to the great masses of people.

Cezar personally informed me that there are already a few groups aiming to build a sort of informational and even practical data base in order to ease the assimilation of the Great Expedition's revelations for the rest of humanity. At the same time, he informed me that there also are groups interested in taking control over any decisions made at the highest level of national security with regards to the Bucegi discovery. Cezar did not see Signore Massini again, but he found out that he and two other "brains" of the world's Masonic elite had more than once been in contact and led significant talks with certain political figures in Romania and, more importantly, in the United States.

In one of my chats with Cezar, after an absence of longer than a year, he told me that both he and General Obadea had felt pressured in regards to this. From this point of view, despite the positive effects of the great discovery and of the expedition, it seems like the "battle between good and evil" intensified even more. The plot is much more complex and contains ultra secret elements which, although I know about it from my conversation with Cezar, I am not allowed to reveal now. But I am sure that there will be a time of "great revelations," and as some signs already show, this is not too far away.

Sometimes, in order to allow for a harmonious and coherent development of events, it is important that we do not "force" things, even if it is possible to do so and the intention is apparently profoundly beneficial. After all, the reality we all live in at a microcosmic level is only the reflection of the universal laws acting on a macrocosmic level. The variations and transformations that happen in our world need to be given a profound meaning and be used wisely in order to avoid any distortions or disturbances of the rhythm.

The present situation of the Romanian people and of the entirety of Mankind is like that of a cancer sufferer. The disease is serious but it can be cured. It is not a simple cold that can be treated immediately. For a cancer patient, avoiding metastasis requires precise and intelligent action. For example, if in his great desire of being cured, the sufferer finds out about a miraculous treatment and applies it immediately, without any discernment, then it is very likely that his body will not cope as it is not ready yet for the influx of healing energy. Hence, he first needs a few preliminary stages of purification and only then can he have the actual treatment that will cure him.

In the same way, the consciousness of the masses, riddled with the complex vices and hardships of modern society, is not always at the necessary level to assimilate correctly certain information and knowledge that could even cause a closing down of its receptivity or a recoil. This is exactly why it is better to wait for the right moment before revealing the shocking truths that Cezar shared with me, especially as they concern our own country as well as humanity as a whole. In other words, this is an issue with a global impact and ample force to penetrate the consciousness of the masses if they are ready to receive it.

On an individual level, the situation is much simpler. When the events we participate in take a spectacular turn, we instinctively feel that destiny is making us ready us for something. We find ourselves, almost uncontrollably, in such circumstances that we are practically forced to adapt as we go to the new path of things, having at the same time a lively interest and intense aspiration in knowing more and acting more efficiently. This is the exact situation I am in now. I only partly know the subtle forces involved and their hidden reasons, but I feel very strongly that they guide me step by step towards a very well defined moment in the future. What I can assert is the amazing intensity of the events I am going to describe in this book and also the fact that it fundamentally transformed my entire being. I am very tempted to believe that my meetings and talks with Cezar, the initiatory explanations he offered, even my being present at the place of the great discovery in the Bucegi Mountains, together with learning about the main aspects of the expedition led by him were only a sort of waiting-room, an absolutely necessary preparation for what I was about to experience afterwards. The facts are well correlated and I intuit that every action is integrated into a larger causal ensemble that is heading towards a certain aim with the precision of a timer.

What I have been faced with exceeds by far even the "illusion" we live during a dream. I must confess that through all of these events, happening in a period of approximately two weeks, a state of complete amazement was permanently present. I can even say that it was the "engine" behind a fundamental transformation of my being, the profoundly spiritual nature of which makes it even harder to describe in precise and eloquent terms. I am aware that what follows might raise a big question mark for some readers and maybe they will even consider it as a fantasy. What can I say in such a situation but that each of us feels and considers as is told by his heart and soul? As far as I am concerned, I feel free and purified of the "fog" of many aspects and realities that I not only never understood but did not even have a clue even existed. I feel and live intensely every moment of my life and I intuit a much more profound meaning to my existence.

Before any of you who are reading this book could doubt its authenticity, I myself have been faced with the impulse of doubt and amazement that often made me wonder if I am dreaming or it is all happening for real. Beyond these mental shocks that I am sure the reader will also experience, I was helped in discerning reality from fantasy and truth from illusion. Even more, I was guided in such a way that these revelations became profound beliefs within my consciousness and the basis of it all. What sustained this essential process was an ample energetic transformation that happened within my being.

I could liken this "miracle" to the situation of a man who fasted for several days, eating nothing and drinking only water. Metaphorically speaking, this is the normal state of ordinary humans who live their lives in an almost larvae-like condition without even suspecting the immense potential capacities that can be accessed instantly if so desired. Of course, at the end of his fast, the man is weak and feeble. Even so, keeping this analogy, he is not aware of the situation he is in, believing that to be his normal state. As soon as he starts eating, he can notice how strong fluxes of energy are flowing through his entire being, infusing him with life force, strength to act, inspiration, will power, happiness and many other feelings and perceptions he was not aware of before. The pointless life, often insipid and limited to prosaic and paltry goals, then vanishes. This is the "miracle" generated by the energetic depths of our being.

I am now capable of better understanding, although still only partially, the consciousness and subtle energetic condition of Cezar Brad as I too live at the present a different life, much richer and effervescent than the one I had before. Before drafting this book, I told Cezar about the amazing things I have been through. In his inimitable way, full of calm and understanding, he was genuinely happy for me and at the same time gave me some precious advice to help with my rapid evolution. I felt he is very satisfied seeing that his choices and efforts concerning me were not without result.

I do not think there is anyone who does not want to be happy and know the mysteries of the universe, but we then have the fundamental question: how do we achieve such a thing? As far as I know, there are many ways; but they all have in common one element: the fact that we are dealing with a process of becoming that takes time. Maybe this is why some people give up on the spiritual path of knowledge right before obtaining a true inner transformation within their being: they are frightened by the effort they need to put into it and the idea of perseverance. In my case, the transformation was extremely rapid and lasted only twelve days. It is likely that, if it lasted longer, my mind would have found some "subversive" ways of attenuating the shock caused by the astounding events I was witness to and then I would have gotten stuck at an inferior level of understanding. Who knows how long I would have had to stay there before my next jump?!

What happened during those sublime twelve days of my life is the subject of the book you are holding now. If I were to refer those days to my own subjective passing of time, I would say I actually lived a couple of years, but in a very condensed way and in a complex dimension of my being. In order to be able to understand that dimension, destiny facilitated my meeting with several beings, not always human, who precisely marked my journey up to my extraordinary meeting with Machandi. That was, without any shadow of doubt, the turning point of my existence. Nothing from then on was the same. Another world, another universe...

Only a few months has passed since then and the intensity of what I lived then and the characteristic vibration never left me for even one moment. That is why I decided to make it known, through this medium, to the readers whose interest might be awakened. There is a reason and a meaning to every aspect of our lives. Maybe in this immense ensemble, my sharing of what happened to me will be like a miraculous cog that will trigger a profound spiritual transformation within your being. During all such transformations it is fundamental to enter the subtle heart...

RADU CINAMAR

ANTENNA STATION

This is an antenna station you can see from the sphinx. It is not part of the secret installation per se, but it shows an official presence of the government in the area. It was a very cloudy day and hard to get a clear picture. Most of the time the antenna was covered in fog.

1

THE MAN THAT TIME FORGOT

A few weeks after *Transylvanian Sunrise* was published, I got a phone call from my editor. We had an understanding that telephone contact to me would only be used in absolutely urgent situations. Due to the nature of the elements presented in the first book, it was to be expected that I would be confronted with various reactions from my readers or certain state organizations. Accordingly, I asked my editor to take care of such correspondence and bring only the most important ones to my attention. I had no idea, however, that this particular phone call was going to turn my life around as fast and as incredibly as it did.

A bit embarrassed, the director of the publishing house explained that for several days in a row he had received regular phone calls on his mobile phone from a man who did not want anything else but to speak to me personally in regard to a very important matter. The editor explained that the man did not give him any more details and did not want to introduce himself either. As the man was very courteous and well mannered, he was politely refused several times under different pretexts. After dozens of such requests, the discussions were firmly ended. Nevertheless, these matters did not have a simple ending.

Just two or three days after their "final" phone conversation, my editor was called once more by the same man whose tone was much firmer but still polite. This time, the energetic impact of the conversation impressed the editor more than the others and he suddenly started to wonder if, after all, it would be opportune to arrange a meeting between me and that person. The decisive element that weighed on his decision was the special mention that the man added at the end of his call. He said that the actual one who so insistently wanted to meet me was a Tibetan lama. That surprised me and I started paying attention.

I asked the editor a few more questions about the identity of the one he spoke to, but his reply was that the man refused to leave his name or any other detail. He only mentioned that it was a very special situation. This is exactly why this respectful but very mysterious person asked for understanding, insisting once more that it was very important that he contact me. Finally, my editor agreed to inform me of the situation without promising that I would consent to any meeting. The man left a mobile phone number in case I decided to accept the offer.

I thanked my editor and assured him that he did the right thing by contacting me. I found the situation intriguing and was becoming a little curious. I had never met a Tibetan lama before; and besides, I was wondering why someone like him would be interested in me. Without waiting any longer and feeling like I was pushed by an unseen force accompanied with a strange inner emotion, I went to a public pay phone and called the number I had written down. After a few rings, a man with a pleasant voice and a slight Transylvanian accent answered my call. I introduced myself and said I was willing to talk if I was told beforehand the purpose of the discussion.

"What I can tell you right now," said the man, "is that we will not have that conversation over the phone. I was myself asked to intermediate a meeting with you, and I want to insist on this meeting's secret nature."

"I have been told that it is a Tibetan lama that wants to speak to me," I said, asking for more details.

"That is true and if you agree, I can give you the address right now," he said, elegantly avoiding any other explanations.

We agreed that we would meet in two days time. I confess that during those two days of waiting I became more and more impatient and interested in the reason behind this meeting. The mysterious aura of the person I spoke with and who had avoided introducing himself was intriguing as was the special importance he gave to this meeting. There was also the prospect that I was going to talk to a Tibetan lama without even knowing the subject of the conversation. All of these things gave me a state of excitement similar to the one I had when I was supposed to meet Cezar for the first time. In a way, my curiosity and restlessness were well founded. Although I suspected it was all related to the great discovery in the Bucegi Mountains, I still could not imagine what the connection with the Tibetan lama was all about.

My confusion was deepened by the fact that Cezar never mentioned anything about a Tibetan knowing about the connecting underground tunnel towards the Tibetan plateau. In the first part of the Great Expedition, which concerned the advance through the Egyptian branch and then through the Tibetan branch, incredible things were discovered – incredible for the beliefs and values of the modern society (these are aspects which, as I have mentioned before, I am not yet allowed to make public); but no human beings were encountered. I found out from Cezar that in the Tibetan area, starting from the tunnel that was leading there, an offshoot was forming towards the surface but it was completely blocked. Topographical studies showed that this particular offshoot of the tunnel was dividing into two, one going towards Mountain Kailasa, where a very old lamasery exists, and the other one going towards Lhasa, the capital, probably having a secret connection with the royal palace. There was another major offshoot from the main tunnel which went in the direction of the Gobi plateau, but this direction had not been pursued in the first stage of the expedition.

Nevertheless, the surprise I was about to experience during this imminent meeting surpassed even my most fantastic expectations. I can certainly say that it was one of the crucial moments that deeply transformed my existence. The unfolding events of the next couple of days were something akin to the effects of shock therapy, ideologically as well as existentially.

Elinor

During the afternoon of the second day after the phone call, I went to the given address. It was a secluded street in an exclusive neighbourhood of Bucharest. The smart houses were shaded by big leafy trees that were moving slowly in the quiet afternoon. I found the house very easily. It was a one story villa that had been recently renovated with a very modern and ingenious design. After ringing the intercom, I was let in almost immediately. A bit nervous, I entered a small courtyard full of greenery with two well cared for paved alleys. Quickly going up a few stairs, I found myself in front of a beautifully carved front door which then fully opened.

At last I was greeted by the mysterious man whose accent I immediately recognized; however, I was quite surprised to notice that he was very young. He did not look older than twenty-six or twenty-seven and was blond, of medium height and was wearing a green shirt and matching trousers. His calm and smiling face invited trust and honesty, but his eyes had hidden depths. Despite his youth, he left me with the impression of being very mature in his gestures and thinking.

Politely inviting me into the living-room, the man introduced himself; but as the meeting happened under confidential terms, I will not divulge his real name. As he knew I would write this book, he suggested I should use the pseudonym Elinor instead of his name.

"In my case though," he said, "this name issue is relative. It is a family 'heirloom' that needs adapting from time to time."

"How so?" I asked, expressing my confusion. "I don't understand — you change your name?"

"I am forced to, so I don't have any troubles," he replied.

"But why? I am honestly surprised," I said, sitting in a leather armchair as I sipped oriental tea that Elinor had offered.

The ambience of the room was wonderful. There was an ingenious design of mixed antique and modern pieces that induced a comfortable feeling of relaxation and high spirits. The young man explained that the lama was going to arrive soon so we began a naturally flowing conversation which soon turned into a series of amazing revelations.

"I knew we would quickly arrive at this point in our discussion," Elinor said. "Under the present circumstances, however, I've decided it is reasonable to share with you a terrible secret, one for whom some would be willing to kill. Besides, this is the main reason why I am so careful with this information, but I know that your integrity is indubitable and your good intentions are wonderful."

I ensured Elinor of my absolute discretion and at the same time made him understand that I was very interested in what he wanted to tell me.

"Soon enough," he went on, "I will have to change my name again as otherwise I would attract some unwanted attention. The reason for this is that my physical appearance does not correspond to my real age."

I was still unable to grasp the essence of the issue.

"Well, I can't see any discrepancy!" I said confidently. "After all, you look very good for a young man of not even thirty."

Elinor was quiet for a while, looking at me very seriously.

"The problem is that I am actually sixty-two," he said very calmly. "I already arouse suspicions in certain people, and I don't want to feed it further. The only way to do this is to completely change my identity and address in Romania. I would probably need to leave the country for a longer period of time as well."

I was left dumbfounded as I looked into the distance. My first thought was that I had let myself be fooled by a crazy man's whim and wasted a few hours of my day. Still, I could not identify the reason why I had to believe that. After all, the man treated me with respect and had been graceful and polite; and even more, his house was an eloquent expression of design and architectural common sense. Except for thinking himself immortal, I had no other reasons to believe that he was crazy.

"I understand your emotional reaction," he said in a detached tone. "After all, it is somehow normal to feel at least slightly skeptical towards what I've told you. If you think deeper though, you will see that it is not impossible for a human being to live more than the present average age limit. Actually, one could live for great periods of time in their physical body."

"What should I draw from that? That you will not die?" I asked him, noticing that I had used the formal way of addressing him after finding out his real age.

"This is for me to discover, isn't it? It will probably be some time before I'll make a decision in this respect," Elinor said in a slightly ironic tone. "My intuition and esoteric knowledge, however, lead me to believe that we cannot remain in the physical body for an indefinite period of time. Even so, physical life can be prolonged for several thousands of years. This can offer extraordinary possibilities of evolution."

As I began to recover from the shocking surprises Elinor was telling me, I remembered the monatomic gold powder found by Cezar in the amphora-shaped vessel in the Projection Room.* At that point, I had not found out what that substance really was. All the explanations I got were just hypotheses and no one had checked if its assimilation would produce a spectacular rejuvenation of the body and at the same time maintain its functioning at optimum parameters for hundreds or even thousands of years. I had no idea if any further research had been done regarding this and did not even know where the precious powder had been eventually transported to.

Not even Cezar himself had told me anything about the white gold when I last met him after his return from the Great Expedition. In turn, I avoided bringing up that subject as I was intuitively aware that it represents a sensitive spot and at the same time a terrible secret. It now seemed, however, that fate was in

---

* *Transylvanian Sunrise* referred to the discovery by Cezar of monatomic gold in the Projection Room. This monatomic gold had a very unique and previously unknown crystalline structure and has been shown to have regenerative effects on living tissues.

my favour as I was finding out about extraordinary things which, without previously rejecting, I would have classified as fantastic. If the person facing me was telling the truth, then I had the living proof that humans do not have to grow old and could even prolong their life in the physical body for a colossal amount of time. I therefore assumed that the secret of the monatomic gold powder was not the exclusive property of an unknown ancient civilization and that Elinor either had a very special connection or was part of the highest elite of global power. Although I doubted this last thought, I voiced my assumption to him.

"I know that the respective powder was one of the hot-spots of the Bucegi Mountains discovery to which you too had access. Maybe you'll be surprised, but I know quite a few details in regards to that and you will soon find out why. As far as I'm concerned, however, my exterior look and longevity are not due to ingesting the monatomic gold powder. What I want to say is that my looks, despite my real age, is not an effect of me using the monatomic gold powder, but it is due to a device which, in my opinion, makes it even more difficult to understand the interaction between men and the energy of time."

I felt another heat wave overcome me as a way of expressing my embarrassment, disbelief and even a sort of panic which caused me to shift restlessly in my seat. I did not want to be the victim of a tasteless farce, but at the same time, I did not have enough arguments to support this suspicion. Still uneasy, I asked for proof. Elinor then showed me his ID card and his passport. I never more closely and carefully examined anyone's identity papers in my entire life, but I could still not find any flaws. There was no doubt over the face in the picture. It was Elinor and the year of birth was very clearly written: 1942. Even so, I thought that the papers might be fake, but I realized that the effort to fabricate them would be too great and the reason behind such an action would be unclear. If he was indeed what he pretended to be, it would have been in his best interests to have papers that proved he was much younger than he is in reality as that would override any disparity with regard to his looks. Intuiting the thoughts I was having, Elinor showed me his original birth certificate and explained that he had already anticipated my reactions which he considered normal under such circumstances. This is exactly why he was all ready to show me his personal documents. It is still hard to explain the complex state of mind I was in just then, knowing that I was facing a man who was not growing old in the conventional sense of the word. The reality before my eyes contrasted with the preconceived and deeply infiltrated ideas from my own mind that kept reminding me that a human being cannot live for hundreds of years, let alone thousands It created a state of confusion for me out of which I almost did not know how to escape.

After what I had already witnessed in the Projection Room, I thought there was nothing left that could cause me surprise or astonishment. And yet here I was again confronted, in the most simple and natural way, with an unsettling element that practically defied the modern scientific ideas and conceptual system in which we have been educated. I could have, of course, adopted the ostrich attitude like so many scientists unfortunately do when something exceeds their capacity to understand. I could have easily left that house, but my experience of similar situations and my profound intuition that the man in front of me was telling the truth encouraged me to accept the "challenge."

Elinor opened the sliding glass wall in the room and let the cool air of the late afternoon come in. His inspired move helped me calm down and order my thoughts.

"OK," I said. "I understand that your situation is a disconcerting truth; but tell me, how did you achieve it? And please do not tell me you were born immortal or I will get up and leave immediately."

Elinor laughed heartily and sat back down in his chair. I had managed to overcome my emotional and even conceptual handicap and this eased the tension in the room. This is also what probably modified our way of addressing each other as we reverted back to an informal atmosphere with common ground.

"I am glad I can reassure you at least in regards to this," said Elinor. "I was born in Oradea* under as normal circumstances as possible. I lived there until I turned 28 when I moved to Bucharest. This was following a crucial event that happened in my life."

I watched him questioningly, inviting him to go on. What I was about to find out shocked me completely.

"At that time, I was just about to start a family of my own. My fiancée was busy organizing the wedding which was going to happen two months later. During one of those days, I received a registered letter, but the name of its sender was unknown to me. The address of the sender was a post office box at one of the post offices here in Bucharest. Intrigued, I opened the envelope and found several finely written pages in a relatively clumsy formulation. I then found out with great amazement that the one writing to me was a forefather of my own family whom neither I nor my parents knew anything about. Yet, in a strange way, the author of the letter seemed to know me very well, mentioning some milestones of my life up to that date and also making some pertinent observations for every member of my family. I was, however, asked not to disclose the content of that letter to anyone as it exposes information that is precious to me.

"If these first elements from the beginning of the letter amazed me, the following ones perplexed me. It seemed that my ancestor was of my father's lineage, but the real issue was that he claimed to have been born in 1424 in Germany in an area that nowadays would be around Cologne. He said that his father was a well-known merchant who travelled several times to Asia Minor for trade. Usually he would travel with his family, but the second time my ancestor accompanied his father, their caravan was attacked and robbed by a gang of thugs. His parents were killed and he, fourteen at the time, was sold as a slave to a king of lesser royalty who ruled over a territory in ancient Persia.

---

* Oradea is a city of a quarter million people in northwestern Transylvania. Formerly a Hungarian city, Oradea rests on the border of Romania and was awarded to Romania after World War I.

"Despite this misadventure, it seems that my ancestor's destiny was still to hold many interesting surprises. A short time after those events, his master was visited by a maharajah from far off India and when this man left, the child was given to him as a slave along with other goods and precious objects. After a long trip in his new master's company, the child arrived in India under the maharajah's domain. It seems that the maharajah was an educated man and very interested in the occult.

"Two years after their return from Persia, a great magician said to possess a terrible power arrived at the court. While visiting the maharajah, the magician was served by the boy and pleased by his behavior and intelligence. Being a friend of the king, he asked for the boy to be given to him when he was ready to leave. In this way, my ancestor became the apprentice of one of the greatest magicians of those times who, as the letter was saying, was actually practicing alchemy, a very secret science whose profound mysteries were known only to the truly wise.

"My ancestor did not mention in the letter if that magician managed to obtain the Philosopher's Stone, the successful culmination of the Alchemical Art, however, he did divulge an unsettling piece of information. He said that although he was in the magician's service for over twenty years, he never noticed any change is his physical aspect or any sign of physical or mental deterioration. In the mean time, he became initiated in quite a few of the alchemical secrets and obtained remarkable progresses on this path. Although he wanted to know more about his master's secret of youth, the latter always avoided the subject.

In the twenty-third year of the apprenticeship, the magician told my relative that they would not see each other again in the their physical form. He did not say why he was leaving or where he was going to. My ancestor was then almost forty and as a last and most precious gift, he received from his master a strange object made out of a special metal alloy. He had been told that as long as he remained around that object, he would never grow old and live for thousands of years. The magician also gave him

THE MAN THAT TIME FORGOT

some valuable advice about how he could obtain that special alloy himself and the needed directions in order to achieve the final shape of the object. That night his master disappeared and was never seen again.

"During the next hundred years, my ancient relative tried on and off to make the mysterious alloy by following his master's instructions. Nevertheless, he confessed in his letter that his joy was so great over knowing that he was not growing old anymore and could live for an indefinite period of time that for many years he preferred to travel and learn many other things. Obtaining the secret alloy fell into second place.

"When he was almost 250 years old, he decided to get married and build a family. He was then in America, on today's California coast. He had three children: two girls and a boy. Having decided to share his secrets with a male heir worthy of it, he discreetly but very carefully kept an eye on the development of his genealogical tree. Due to the extensive life experience already accumulated, he started devoting himself to thoroughly studying various oriental spiritual currents, gradually abandoning his travels and social life. For five generations worth of his family tree, he closely followed the life of the male heir that seemed the strongest. When necessary, he would mysteriously assist, in more or less occult ways, the continuity of his genealogical tree.

"He already possessed immense wealth and his scholarly documentation was housed in a grand library. Due to a very well thought out system, he managed not to raise any suspicions about his wealth, which was spread across countless places across the earth, or about the fact that he was not growing old. When he was among others, it was essential not to stand out in society and to change his identity and address as often as possible in order not to raise questions. Still, because of a complicated situation he was involved in around 1900, he came very close to being exposed and had to resort to extreme solutions. Living in Australia for almost fifteen years, he managed to cover his tracks. The unpleasant surprise was that once he was back in a Europe eaten by the First World War, my ancestor became aware that his family, including his last male heir, was missing. The head of the family and his direct male heir had been killed in war and the rest of the family, including two boys, were missing."

Elinor then took a break to close the window. It was dark outside and cold. I was so fascinated by his account that I only noticed the cold when he stopped. Gladly accepting another cup of hot tea, I impatiently waited for him to take me back to the magic of the incredible story.

"My Tibetan friend will arrive any moment now," Elinor said, eyeing his watch. "Now comes the part that will somehow clarify my situation. There are still a few more surprises for tonight," he said smiling.

Although very interested in the rest of the story, I still asked Elinor for the reason why the Tibetan priest wanted to meet me.

"I've been asked not to divulge anything before his arrival," he replied. "Soon all your questions will be answered."

Happy with this outcome, I waited for him to continue his amazing story.

"My ancestor was almost 500 by then. Of course, as his master assured him, he not only did not grow old but even became younger than when he received the mysterious alloyed object. During the four centuries that passed, it is probable that his perspective and way of perceiving the world changed profoundly. His consciousness was greatly elevated, but his priorities became totally different. In simple yet very powerfully emotional words, he was telling me that he managed to achieve the ultimate desire of any genuine alchemist: he obtained the Philosopher's Stone. He explained that it would not have been possible without him first profoundly understanding the essence of life and the universe themselves as well as other mysteries of knowledge that had been revealed to him during his existence. As far as I figured it out, his big breakthrough happened while living in Australia.

"Coming back to Europe, he renewed some contacts and connections he had in France. It seems there was already a small group of people that had been gradually initiated by him into very occult aspects of science and spirituality. It was known that he was an accomplished alchemist, but no one could say for sure where his true origins were. Parallel to his investigations of his heir's family, he wrote two books about the mysteries of the alchemical symbols and a few other manuscripts about the esoterics of forms and coded languages. It seems these manuscripts were very secret, being destined to a small number of disciples. The books have been published in France by his main alchemy student who is also a fine scientist.

"The experience of his few centuries of living showed my ancestor that it is not at all easy to swiftly travel in time, especially in modern society. The more technological the world and the more complex the communications, the more difficult it became to justify his presence for very long in any given place. He confessed in the letter that the profound transformation that happened to him made him understand that he had a spiritual mission he could no longer ignore. This, however, was becoming increasingly difficult as he could no longer appear in public, had to often change his identity and home, and had to be very careful with anyone he chose to take his messages into the world.

"Paradoxically, the immortality – which for many people is extremely desirable and envied – could even seem oppressive in modern society. As far as I understand, this is just from a selfish perspective as, generally speaking, man wants to solely enjoy the various pleasures and opportunities that a very long life and unaltered youth could offer. But, I will ask you to remember an essential point and that is that the precious gift of fabulous longevity must not be wasted. That is why the fundamental element is that of responsibility and the necessity of harmonizing the opposites. This involves a profound understanding of life and of the main goal of human existence.

"My ancestor was saying that these aspects became clear for him while he was in Australia when he was contacted though occult channels by the representatives of a superior civilization and hierarchy concerning our planet. He could not mention anything else about this, but as far as I would be interested and if I were to follow his instructions, a time would come when I would learn all the details.

"Because his achievements in alchemy were total, it was fairly easy for him to obtain the very complicated alloy that the object ensuring his immortality was made of. He wrote that he even discovered a simpler way of producing it but mentioned that the special shape of the object had to remain unchanged. He suspected I was curious as to what determines the extension of physical life when a human being was around that object; and he explained that in order to understand, I first needed firm esoteric knowledge. In principle, he said he could call it a phenomenon of tuning the alloy's frequency of vibration to the specific frequency of vibration of the human body. In other words, a kind of subtle energetic mutual interaction was created between the metal object and the being in its vicinity.

"He specified, however, that the longevity effect was only valid for the one the object was destined to. That is to say, the object had to be made by a master alchemist, it being strictly personalized. Its effect was only for the respective person as it had the specific subtle imprint of the organism of that being. The secret alloy also had the particular and exceptional property of favoring the subtle energetic connection with the center of universal life, but it was also selecting the access to this formidable energy according to and just for the designated person. It seems that the secret of how to obtain this alloy comes from times immemorial, from predynastic Egypt, having been offered to the great priests of the time by the gods that came upon Earth.

"The true art of making the object, particularly the alloy — which is composed of several metals and substances — consists of tuning the energetic frequencies of vibration so as to personalize the object. This art was a complete secret which could not be known by anyone else but a master in alchemy. This is why, as far as I understood in reading the letter, that the secret was shared with just one person who was chosen to be the one who would continue the respective initiatory line. Besides, the method of obtaining the alloy requires certain exceptional knowledge and inner capabilities and it cannot work unless the being is truly prepared, from a spiritual point of view, to do it. Only then did I figure out why my ancestor could not obtain this alloy in his previous attempts – it was because he hadn't yet reached that level of elevation and profound knowledge of the mysteries of Creation.

"Still, he confessed that before obtaining the Philosopher's Stone, he had already obtained the life elixir, a stage that naturally precedes the accomplishment of the Great Alchemical Work. He revealed that the elixir of life is a ruby colored liquid which, when administered with precise science, allows an extension of life in the physical body of three to four times more than the effect of the mysterious alloy object. When given the object, his master told him that it will ensure him approximately 1700-2000 years of terrestrial life, time enough for him to make gradual progress in alchemy and thus discover the elixir of life.

"I gathered from this that the master first making and then giving the object to his favorite disciple was in a way a spiritual lineage, a special tradition with origins in a very distant past of humanity. Besides, considering the period of time in a physical body that this alloy makes possible, I assume that there were only fifteen to twenty individuals in the lineage of this very mysterious tradition that possessed the object. In my approximate calculations, I count on the fact that most of the owners advanced to the next superior stage long before the deadline, maybe after 500 to 700 years of terrestrial life. Of course, it is just a supposition, but these numbers may very well signify the average time that they possessed the object. Even so, this shows that the tradition is at least 7000-8000 years old which exceeds by far any other tradition of any other spiritual path known and practiced nowadays."

I interrupted him here to voice an insistent thought.

"Tell me, shall I gather from this that you are the one carrying on the tradition?"

"As far as I know, there is only one person on this planet that has had the object for a period of time. I found out from my ancestor that every master must leave that special alloy object TO JUST ONE PERSON, his most trusted disciple. When the disciple considers that he has found the right person, he will, in turn, give it to him. This is a practice that involves great responsibility. My ancestor took a more unusual approach by following through time the evolution of the main branch of his family tree. After all, there was nothing keeping him from looking over the next thousand years for another being worthy of such a secret if none of the progeny of his family tree would rise to meet his demands. Destiny made it that I was the last male descendant of the main branch of my family which was of interest to my ancestor."

"But, you said earlier that he lost track of the last family of this branch," I remarked.

"It's true, but after a few years of discrete investigations and thanks to some high connection that he had, he managed to identify the place where this family was. After the husband's death on the battle field, the mother and four children took refuge in Germany with some relatives. Unfortunately, one of the girls died in an accident; and one year after that, the mother disappeared and was never heard of again. Around 1932, because of political tensions in Germany, the family of relatives that adopted the children emigrated to Romania in northern Transylvania and settled in Oradea two years later. Of the two boys, one was very weak, suffering from tuberculosis and dying of it a few years later. The other one was my father who got married and started his own family in Oradea. I was the only child they had."

"Now I understand," I said. "I wonder though what the masters of this tradition are doing after they hand over the object."

"I don't know for sure either," answered Elinor. "It seems that it is a great secret and my ancestor didn't say anything about it. What I know is that, using the elixir of life, they go on living in their physical body for millennia afterwards. Still, the reasons they do that are not yet clear to me. Most probably, they have spiritual missions to fulfill that require their physical presence. Logically, this means they keep on living more or less hidden among the other inhabitants of this planet but I suspect that it is a bit more complicated than that. It is also possible that only some of my predecessors took this line of action and some did not. You see, these are questions whose answers I will probably find out much later."

We were both quiet for a while, mentally analyzing various possibilities. Eventually, I decided to ask him a question.

"This means that the object is here in the house?"

"Yes, of course," Elinor replied. "Its radius of influence is a few meters. It is not absolutely necessary to always be around it, but if I want the effects to be constant, I have to keep it close most of the time. You can compare it with a special antenna that acts as a resonator. In the beginning, those who received the apparatus probably knew much more about its origins, specifics and way of functioning; but with the passing of millennia, we lost some of the information."

"OK, but how did you get the object?" I asked curiously. "Did you meet your ancestor?"

"I didn't meet him then although I truly wished it. My impression was that he avoided meeting me mostly because of the watchfulness of the Romanian secret services who all throughout the Seventies started to behave quite drastically. Personally, I'm convinced that my ancestor's never been to Romania but that he contacted me through some very discreet intermediaries. It was clear then, and I have fully convinced myself since, that whomever finds themselves in my situation needs to be very careful if they want to perpetuate this occult tradition. The reason why is obvious. There are people and even secret societies who know about this lineage of alchemical masters and who greatly desire to find out the mysteries of obtaining the alloy. Fortunately, this is a very well kept secret, and even if known, the alloy cannot be obtained without the understanding of certain subtle keys that are essential in the respective alchemical process. For example, in one of the transmutation stages, you get a metal with very special properties that contemporary scientists are not even aware of. The temptation of extending the physical life is too great for some and they will try to achieve eternal life by all means and at all costs. It is therefore obvious that I need to be very cautious."

"You mean your life is in danger," I said.

"Yes. I have ensured myself of a very long life compared to the average human life, on the condition that my vital functions are not interrupted.

"But let me come back to the letter. I remember that while I was reading it, I was torn by two conflicting tendencies: on the one hand, I felt like tearing and throwing away the letter as I thought someone was mocking me; but on the other hand, I felt like what was written there was true. Besides, it was all too complicated to be just a farce. And then, what would be the reason for anyone to do this to me? I was just a normal man with a regular life and without any high expectations.

"At the end of the letter was mentioned the procedure I had to follow to the letter. Without letting anyone know, without packing anything, without leaving any suspicion that something out of the ordinary happened, I was to go to a certain address in Bucharest at a certain date and time, not sooner or later. The directions were to enter straight into the mentioned house.

"Initially, I was overcome by panic, and I even intended to hand the letter over to the police who at that time were called the militia. But that wouldn't have solved anything as the letter only contained a story without any actual data that would lead to identifying the one who wrote it. Going to the police would have gotten me involved in a never-ending series of interrogations and harassment specific to the modus-operandi of the communist regime. I asked myself then, "What was there to lose if I followed the instructions?" Even if I would have chosen to go to the police and they busted into that address in Bucharest, I was pretty sure they wouldn't have found anything there. The whole operation was too well planned to allow for such mistakes. Even more, I was confident that any move I made was being discreetly watched and this was to be read between the lines in the letter as well.

"I quickly decided to go to Bucharest, following the directions closely. I took that decision by myself although the old attachments and habits were still trying to draw me back. An obscure fear was pervading my heart, but the appeal of the extraordinary chance I was given was stronger than the incertitude. Strangely, although I knew I was offered a life of almost 2000 years, I had no actual thoughts about what I was going to do. I was thinking that I should come with various plans, ideas, and desires; but instead, it was as if my mind was paralyzed at the thought that I might live in this physical body for thousands of years.

"In short, I got to Bucharest and found the address quite quickly. It was a four storey block of flats in a quiet neighbourhood. As I read in the letter, the door was unlocked. I entered a one bedroom flat that was modestly furnished and it seemed like no one was there. On the living room table was, in a big envelope, a paper with directions, a key and an enormous amount of money for those times. I was told to leave that place immediately and go to another address in Bucharest which this time was a house. I should remain there for three days until contacted by a certain someone. The key was for the house and the money for expenses. Counting the money, I realized that it was enough for me to live comfortably for one year. I was advised though not to leave the house unless absolutely necessary. The fridge was also generously stocked with food. It seemed like it was all part of a movie script, but what I was asked to do was quite easy. I was engrossed in thoughts for a while and then re-read the directions. It looked like everything was already set up to offer me an unending existence."

"Still, your life in this physical body was going to end after approximately 2000 years," I said.

"Indeed. It seems that the effect of the alloy is weaker than the alchemical elixir, but as far as I know, no one lived the maximum period that the object offers. Therefore, a direct verification of this theory, probably coming from the beginning of the tradition, is missing. We can't be sure that the message hasn't altered with the passing of time."

"But where was the object?" I asked impatiently. "Was it brought by a person you met?"

"Things were a bit more complicated. After I settled in the other house, which was also in a quiet neighbourhood but on the other side of town, I waited for the intermediary. The place was very comfortable, bordering on luxurious, but I noticed there was no phone. The cable was there but there was no handset. Maybe that was a security measure so I would not try to contact someone. Just as I had been told, the intermediary arrived after three days. While waiting for him, I spent my time reading and watching TV. In order to avoid creating any kind of troubles, I refrained from going out. At the end of that period, I was a little bored but the curiosity and interest for what was coming were still with me.

"The respective person who arrived was a mature gentleman who confirmed that he was sent by my ancient relative. Although I overwhelmed him with a torrent of questions, he remained inflexible. All that he told me was to just be patient and have trust. He then took out a camera from his bag and asked me to stand in front of an empty wall. After he took my picture, he noticed that I was confused. In order to avoid an unpleasant scene, he explained that the photos were necessary for my new identification documents. He then told me that he would be back in three days and that I needed to be ready to go by then.

"At this point, I contemplated going back to the ordinary life I seemed to be so easily giving up. The feeling of uncertainty I was experiencing, compounded by a lack of information, made me realize that the situation could be dangerous. Why would I need another set of identification documents? But particularly, what sort of documents were we talking about? After all, my ID card and driver's licence were still valid and a passport was out of the question as Romanian citizens of those times were not allowed to possess such a document.

"Only then did it suddenly dawn on me that I was going to leave the country; but not by illegally crossing the border; but by actually passing through one of the border crossings with a legal and valid passport. My heart shrunk under the waves of emotion and fear that gripped my imagination. I could already see myself caught, locked up and beaten in the cellars of the feared National Security, subjected to unending, exhausting and often very violent interrogations. I was nervously pacing through the house, not knowing what to do. My logic was telling me that because Romanian citizens were not allowed to own a passport, it meant that I was going to have a fake ID under a different nationality. Sweating profusely, I threw myself on the bed. I was musing that I had just uselessly complicated my life just before building a decent future for myself with a family and maybe, as much as possible in a communist country, a career. And for what? After all, my life was good for as long as it would have lasted. I did not need one or two thousand years during which time I would most definitely become tired!

"Obviously, all of those thoughts were just my preservation instinct pushing me, as much as still possible, on the path of mediocrity and banality. After a while, I started to calm down and get another perspective on the issue at hand. For example, I had to admit that my ancestor always respected my free will. In no way or form had he forced me to take a certain decision. It had always been my choice just as it actually still was at this new moment. Even then, at least apparently, I was still free to abandon it all and resume my previous life without anyone losing out or suffering. I would have quickly found an explanation for my fiancée and family, and the impressive amount of money I would have brought back would have made everyone happy.

"On the other hand, my ancestor would have remained as inaccessible and unknown as he was to that day, and I'm pretty sure that all of the arrangements made by him through all of these mysterious intermediaries wouldn't have provided any clues to the authorities. I was forced to admit that, due to the wisdom, experience and connections accumulated during his lengthy life, my ancestor was able to act from a distance in a very intelligent and practically flawless way. He must have predicted the eventuality of my abandonment, but he did so with an amazing delicacy as he was prepared to reward me for all of the 'inconveniences' I had experienced by giving me that huge amount of money.

"My final conclusion was that I had to make my own destiny. At the same time, I was starting to see that instead of always and selfishly asking for proof of what was written in the letter – and I'm referring here to the mysterious personalized object – it was first of all necessary that I show at least a minimal proof of deserving it. Instead of having an inquisitorial attitude and way of thinking, as if eternal life was my birth right without any effort, it was much wiser to realize that what I was going to be offered was actually of an inestimable richness for my destiny as well as an extraordinary opportunity for my evolution. Otherwise, I would have been in danger of not appreciating the true value of my ancestor's present; and without any doubt, my ignorance could have caused enough mistakes to cost me my life."

"I understand perfectly," I said. "I know these aspects as they have also been presented to me as a result of other circumstances — by a very special person."

Elinor smiled understandingly.

"I think you are talking about Mr. Cezar Brad, aren't you? Indeed, it seems he is a being that has achieved a high degree of consciousness," Elinor said thoughtfully. "You too are part of this complex mechanism involving remarkable beings. Shortly, you will realize that nothing in life is by chance and that events correlate and synchronize in ways that are often astonishing for the common human being. It is a great art to see these synchronicities and then understand their hidden meaning. At the same time, if you can do that, it is a clear sign that you have evolved.

"But, let me come back to what I was saying. Upon more reflection from my part over these aspects, I was gradually becoming firmly convinced that I was supposed to lead a certain life

THE MAN THAT TIME FORGOT

and one that was closely related to my ancestor. So, I decided to fully abandon myself to the plan that the great alchemist had prepared for me in every detail. There were some risks of course, but my decision was already unshakable. I still had a few slight hesitations at first due to the attachment I had towards my fiancé and my family, but I calmed down by telling myself that I would still have all the time in the world to go back to them. Inside of me, however, I knew perfectly well that it would never happen.

"After three days, the gray-haired man came back as sombre and as calm as the first time. As I suspected, there was a forged passport that I was going to use to cross the border. My expectations were exceeded, however, when I noticed that it was a diplomatic passport and that I was listed as a Belgian citizen. The gentleman explained that it was made so because of my knowledge of French which made it all the more credible for the border officials. He was going to accompany me to Brussels and we were flying there the next afternoon. To be a bit more concise, everything went well and the customs officers even wished us a 'bon voyage!' By night fall, I was already settled in a very luxurious villa in the capital of Belgium, somewhere in a residential area of the city. The man that accompanied me retreated discreetly after making sure that I had everything I needed. He also told me that I was going to be visited by someone special later that evening.

"I smiled lightly. This was probably going to be the moment of my long awaited meeting with my relative. I have to admit that sometimes life changes so quickly and spectacularly that you need a lot of discernment and self-control in order to cope as much as possible. A week earlier, I was planning a family together with my fiancé in Oradea, Romania. Now I was in Belgium with another identity and waiting to meet a relative a couple hundred years old. Quite shocking, isn't it?"

Elinor laughed casually and got up to turn the light on. It was almost dark outside and the Tibetan lama had not arrived yet. With the magic of his story now interrupted for the time being, I noticed the time and was startled.

"It is quite late. Do you think there will still be a meeting tonight?" I asked skeptically.

"Without any doubt," answered Elinor, "although I am a bit surprised by this delay myself. Let's be patient. He will arrive shortly and you will then be faced with a great surprise."

I could not understand any of these mysteries, but Elinor promised that there would not be too long of a wait.

"If so, please continue your story and tell me what happened that evening in Brussels," I said, settling as comfortable as I could in my armchair and tasting one of the cookies I had been offered.

"I met the master alchemist, my ancestor. I was nervous, but he seemed to understand me very well and thanked me for trusting him and his letter. He looked approximately 32-33 years old and, please believe me, I was bewildered and trying to justify what was happening to me as being a farce, it being impossible that someone looking like the man facing me could have already lived for longer than 500 years. I immediately expressed my doubts. He looked at me, calmly and seriously, and asked what exactly I thought a 500 year old man should look like. That rendered me quiet and I realized the ridiculousness of the situation.

"He then went on to tell me that I would not be able to convince myself of the existence of the secret society and the extraordinary effect the mysterious object has on the lives of those it was made for until a few decades pass. My ancestor advised me to use this waiting time actively, educating myself and learning the mysteries of alchemy in order to be capable of ascending to the next higher stage of my evolution. He offered to show and provide me everything I needed in order to do that.

'I can feel that you have a remarkable potential,' my ancestor said, 'but even so, you will see that those starting out on the path of this tradition differently integrate the time they have at their disposal, time that is much longer than the life of an ordinary man. That is

54

why your progress in the alchemical sciences will be quite slow. It is possible to be hundreds of years old, maybe even thousands of years old, until you reach total fulfilment in your alchemical work. During this very long period of time, you might have to cope with major transformations, maybe even dramatic ones, but all of these will help you gather immense experience that will fully contribute to the complexity of your destiny.

'You could ask me,' he said, 'how is it possible that some alchemist could manage to reach the highest achievements of their work in just one ordinary life time? This is indeed possible; but in such cases, they are already born with high merits on this path, having achieved them in previous lives. I'm almost sure that you are not familiar with aspects of metempsychosis or those referring to the esoteric laws of action and reaction within the universe. That's why the explanations I'm going to give you now might seem hilarious and illogical, but you will then have plenty of time to understand and observe these aspects. It's good for you to know though that the extraordinary longevity that is now yours can offer you the possibility of evolving spiritually much faster than following the cycles of birth and death that other people go through.'

"My ancestor stopped and watched me carefully to see what reactions his words generated," continued Elinor. "I was incapable of uttering any words as I couldn't understand the significance of what he told me. Now I know exactly what my ancestor meant. These are basic aspects he was explaining. At that time of my life, however, they were a completely unexplored subject to me."

Elinor stopped his narration to ask me how familiar I was with these notions. I told him that I did not know much about it, but I would appreciate it if he could tell me more.

Destiny and Reincarnation

"You know very well that the issue of reincarnation causes controversy even nowadays although there is countless evidence that proves this truth," said Elinor. "The need to maintain as effective control as possible over people has caused some leaders in the shadows of political and economical forces to orient science and the education of the masses towards a very simple and concise conclusion: there is no soul; there is no spirit; and after the demise of the physical body, nothing happens as it all returns into nothingness. In other words, according to this modern 'ideology,' someone disappears completely when they die and without a trace.

"Although aberrant and even lacking logic, this idea caught on and a large majority embraced it, mainly because they feel it saves them from useless troubles and complicating their lives. Some even slip into a very wrong mentality that can throw them into the depths of desperation. In other words, they think that if 'we only have one life' and there is nothing else afterwards, it means they can commit all kinds of acts. This applies in particular to evil and even abominable acts, done for purely selfish reasons, as they will not have to pay for them after they die. You can see how this can be a real problem, and it is not by chance that the modern society is confronted with an unprecedented wave of vices and crime. The fight for justice is just on the surface as it can't crush it in the bud. The ideology perpetrated upon us is corrupt and false but is kept so deliberately to cause chaos and to allow the elite to control everything they possibly can."

"I am aware of these aspects, of course," I said. "But your ancestor's perspective on the possibility of a more rapid evolution is interesting."

"Yes, the extension of life while in the physical body is extraordinary," commented Elinor. "At a glance, it might look like it takes a very long time to get a certain result while others, living a normal life, obtain the same effects in just a few years or tens of years. In reality, they are only continuing what they started many lives before.

"Let's imagine the following situation. I start to study the mysteries of alchemy. At the same time as me, another ordinary man living a normal life time is initiated on the same path. Let's also assume that we both progress at about the same pace. After a few tens of years, he will inevitably die and his soul — carrying (among others things) the quintessence of all of the knowledge he has gathered up to that point — will translate into a superior level of Creation. For most human beings, this level is represented by the subtle astral universe which is much broader than the physical universe."

Elinor took a short break to have a sip of tea. He then continued with his explanations.

"People do not die in the true sense of the word. I mean, they do not disappear into nothingness. They only abandon their physical 'carcasses,' their bodies of flesh and bones that rot. Only the physical body 'dies.' The subtle part of the being, the soul, translates into another space-time dimension of the Creation that is most favorable for its continued existence. That is why it is said that there's no such thing as 'death.' The human being, as an individual entity, never disappears but translates from one level of Creation to another. This is the same as getting out of a car and getting on a train; then getting off the train and getting onto a ship. The analogy can go on and on. In each of these situations, you have a specific way of getting from one place to another and a certain degree of freedom.

"When comparing a physical body to a mode of transport, it is, we could say, what you can afford at that moment: what you saved to pay for the ticket, be it for the bus, train or ship. If you didn't save enough; that is, if you don't have too many merits, then you walk. If you are very 'rich,' you can then afford a ticket for even a spaceship! Analytically speaking, in this latter situation, you have access to a very elevated subtle world. If you only have a few merits because your mistakes were many or great, then the subtle dimension that your soul is projected into after the death of the body will be one full of anguish and suffering. These demarcations refer to the destiny of every human and are in full accordance to the actions, good or bad, that the respective being committed either in his terrestrial existence or in the subtle worlds. If none of this were so, there would be no difference between the worldly condition of a saint and a criminal nor a mentally retarded person and a genius. Common sense tells us that it is not by chance that a human being is born with a severe physical handicap while another is perfectly healthy and thriving; or that some suffer from childhood with all sort of anguishes, fears, and nightmares while others are happy, optimistic and very joyful. I think you understand very well what I'm saying. Still, people's incredible superficiality and even stupidity prevents them from seeing these very simple and obvious circumstances. This is exacerbated by their almost sick dependency on automated belief systems and prejudices that have been imposed since childhood. All of this contributes to their physical and moral decay as well as to their incapability of understanding certain essential truths about the life they're living."

"Yes, I have often been faced with this opaque public opinion," I observed bitterly. "But you know, I've noticed that it is not necessarily people's enmity but the fact that they are confronted with the decision of replacing the materialistic ideas that they have been inoculated with since school with something that almost everyone ridicules and says does not exist. Of the two options, most choose to keep their old beliefs even if they feel that something is not OK. The idea of nothing quantitative to measure, compounded by lack of physical or mental effort, most often succeeds in defeating their spiritual throb. In such circumstances, that in my opinion accentuate selfishness and eat away effectivity, you can't expect to obtain too many merits. Life ends relatively quickly and what follows is, so to speak, 'the reaping.'"

Elinor immediately picked up my idea.

"That's exactly what I was talking about," he said. "What the man does during his terrestrial life forces him to somehow return to the physical level after his 'stay' in the astral level where the soul lives in a world attuned to its specific 'wavelength.' For example, due to his desire to succeed in the alchemical arts, the person in our earlier example will reincarnate in such circumstances so as to favor his access to this knowledge. Of course, setting the course of destiny for a soul just about to return to the physical level is very complex and requires extremely precise work on behalf of cosmic entities infinitely superior to the common and rational way of human thinking. Everything is considered out of the immense baggage of actions, experiences, emotions and intentions that every human being gathers during their countless existences in manifestation and those tendencies will essentially define the course of their destiny in the next incarnation. Such choices are based upon certain criteria; and the being is going to experience in his new physical life a sort of 'response' to the actions he did in other terrestrial lives."

"Yes. I often wondered exactly how this process of 'accounting' for our actions happens, but I could never find the answer," I said pensively.

Elinor was quiet for a minute after which he answered me very competently.

"Every action, be it done with the body or the mind, is mysteriously 'recorded' in what the occultist calls the 'cosmic memory,'" Elinor explained. "The quintessence of these actions is then impregnated at the level of the individual soul, being either a 'burden' or a 'delight' for the one living out his destiny. Man's fate is not at all by chance but in full accord with the nature of his actions, and this is exactly why people are born so differently. Each needs to live out his own destiny according to the nature of his actions. Good deeds will attract merits; and as a consequence, that being will enjoy wonderful circumstances, chances and situations in its incarnation at the physical level while bad deeds will attract nefarious consequences, much suffering and torment for the respective being. It is important to know that these 'rewards' are at the same time the perfect balance between action and recompense. No one is privileged and no one is disadvantaged. Each gets exactly what he deserves even if many say they've been aggrieved and choose to blame God for giving them so much suffering and troubles. Why do they have to toil on the edge of subsistence while others luxuriate in richness and wealth? These kinds of questions are frequent in those who live a hard life but do not understand the causes of their suffering. As I was saying, situations like the ones mentioned represent the faithful image of the compensatory law balancing out the actions that have been previously done. Those who are not sufficiently spiritually awakened, however, do not yet know or understand these matters."

I was very interested in these topics as it allowed me to synthesise my initiatory knowledge. I then asked Elinor what it is exactly that determines a future reincarnation of the soul at a terrestrial level.

"During the time between two successive reincarnations," he continued, "the individual soul lives in an astral world in accordance with the merits he obtained. When these are exhausted, the time comes for other actions done during his previous terrestrial existences to 'ripen' and receive their 'reward,' be it good or bad, in the physical world as a new reincarnation. This 'condensation' of destiny's requirements attracts the soul irresistibly towards the physical level and into a 'matrix' or social integration pattern that is most appropriate for the specific nature of the actions that need to be compensated. The future human being that's going to be born into that matrix is either going to consume the good fruits or merits of their beneficial actions of the past or else pay for their previous deeds and the suffering caused to others. Most often, there is a combination of the two and this explains why people are born with certain qualities but also with certain physical or psychic defects. Still, it's up to them as to how they 'organize' their destiny. In other words, they are the ones generating, through the actions done in their present life, the nature of their destiny in future reincarnations."

"Well...but in this case, there's practically no end to the cycle of reincarnations!" I exclaimed. "Whether we do good deeds or bad ones, we will be reborn into eternity in order to consume the fruits of our actions."

"This is only on the surface," Elinor answered. "The fundamental difference between good and bad actions is that the first bring you closer to God while the latter avert you from Him. The salvation or liberation talked about in genuine religions consists exactly of reabsorbing into a dimension that transcends even this apparently never-ending cycle of life and death which is like a chain of dependencies. Following the path of evolution, always synonymous with good and harmony, the man eventually reaches the end of the road and then something inconceivable for the ordinary consciousness happens. It's like a passing, a leap into the infinite that includes all worlds but at the same time is outside of them too.

"I wouldn't want to deviate too much now on this thread of our conversation as the initial idea we started from was different. In the comparative example I chose previously, I said that the one who was initiated into the mysteries of alchemy reaches a certain level of understanding in this existence. After that, he dies and his soul will project for a period of time into one of the subtle worlds of the astral level."

"Do we all translate into the astral level after we die at the physical one?" I asked, eager to clear this aspect that I did not understand.

"This occurs for most human beings by reason of the fact that the astral level is a level of emotions and psychic manifestations which, as you know, represent the fundamental aspects that define the life of a human being. Still, if some have already reached a very elevated level of consciousness, their soul will automatically be attracted, after their physical death, to even more subtle levels of manifestation such as the mental or even causal level. Here, the nature of reality is much more subtle and vast than the astral level. For example, there is practically nothing in the causal level that we could associate with ordinary sight or thinking. The mind is completely transcended and knowledge is no longer a discursive action but a total and simultaneous one. There, the individual consciousness has access to the archetypes of Creation as well as the causes that determine the manifestation of things and phenomena within the inferior levels, including the physical world. This is why the one who exists in this extremely elevated level of manifestation can control anything within the manifested world as he is then capable of 'doing and undoing,' from its causal origin, any action, plan or intention. It goes both ways though. If, during their earthly existence, the being has made great mistakes such as blameworthy acts of despotism, physical and psychic oppression, crimes, or very violent acts; then their soul will be inexorably attracted after death towards the dark infernal dimensions of the inferior astral level where they will have to pay for their deeds. Don't get me wrong, we are not talking about eternal damnation; but these kinds of actions have great influence on personal destiny; and this is why the period of time spent in the inferno – in order to compensate it seems — is very long in terrestrial years.

"A rather special situation is that of suicides as their suffering is extremely long and the evolutionary regress is considerable. In such dramatic cases, the soul hardly realizes that just this one reckless act of their earthly existence can cost thousands of years of suffering and involution. If one were capable of giving themselves back the life they also took, it would not be such a problem; but it does not happen like that, and this is why the torments a suicidal soul must endure are excruciating. A suicide is, in essence, self-denial taken to the extreme and is much more serious then the ignoring of the divine spark or divine spirit within us. An atheist still has the chance of evolving and changing his opinion during his lifetime while a suicide very selfishly puts an end, by his own volition, to the chance he has been given to evolve in this existence. Such a soul did not understand a fundamental aspect I have mentioned earlier: namely, that even when a being feels overwhelmed at some point in his life by his troubles, suffering or problems he faces, all of these are nothing else but the nature of the actions he did in the past. The ordeals and miserable life he endures now are, with very few exceptions, the exact image of the suffering he has caused to others. Consequently, his reckless act is a selfish attempt of cheating destiny; or better said, of avoiding it, thinking that this way he will not have to endure it anymore. This is why the gravity of suicide is enormous and constitutes a major obstacle on the evolutionary path, maybe the biggest of all.

"On the other hand, there are some souls that have been very attached to the material things of their terrestrial life or that have been very parsimonious and paltry in their relationships with others. At an ethereal level, they stay for quite a long period of time in the immediate vicinity of the places and things they are attached to. The ethereal level, as you know, is a frequency of vibration between the physical and the astral level. The state of these souls is aboulic as they do not realize what is happening with themselves, and the only thought that dominates is the desire of returning to the things, material possessions or even beings they have been much attached to during their physical life. Such beings spend most of their time engulfed in a sombre atmosphere, like a thick fog. They remain at this subtle level for a very long time, a subtle level found in the immediate vicinity of our planet. From time to time, due to their gross desires and earthly attachments, they haunt the respective places in an ectoplasmic form which imitates faithfully, more or less, the body shape they had in their last physical existence. This pathetic condition can sometimes last for hundreds of years; until their understanding gradually lights the twilight that surrounds them; and they are thus finally freed from the grip of their attachments. This is a typical example of consuming certain attachment-related karma. After all this, the respective soul will ascend to an astral level far superior to the deplorable condition they were in at the ethereal level. Of course, where they end up at the astral level will fully depend on other aspects corresponding to the individual destiny of that soul. After spending a while consuming their specific merits for that astral world, they will reincarnate into a physical body and the process will start all over again but on a superior level of individual experience."

"OK," I said. "Now it is clear, but does life at the subtle levels last as long as the life an ordinary man lives at the terrestrial level? Because...you said that, after the death of the body, every soul spends a certain period of time in one of the subtle levels of manifestation."

"Time," Elinor replied, "as universal subtle energy, is perceived differently on different levels of Creation. For example, at the astral level, time does not have the same meaning or same 'flow' as at the physical level. What you perceive here as a precise duration of time is much distorted there. The more elevated the level of manifestation, the more nuanced the perception of time. The fact that the respective level is multidimensional determines the complex phenomena of synchronicity and simultaneity of events. Time cannot be judged anymore by its 'physical' parameters.

"The average astral 'stay' of the individual soul between two successive incarnations ranges from 50 to 300 terrestrial years, according to their achieved merits. Of course, there are exceptions depending upon the decisions of some superior hierarchical forums of celestial entities; but generally speaking, this is the period of time most individual souls spend at the astral level after the death of their physical body."

"So, in your example," I said, "the one who was initiated into the mysteries of alchemy and then dies returns to the physical world when you are already 300-400 years old! I now understand the meaning of your path."

Elinor approved, nodding slightly.

"Yes," he replied, "but by then I've already progressed much more as I have used the time his soul spent at the astral level to continuously perfect myself. When, after the death of the body, the soul translates into the subtle worlds, it is subjected there to other kinds of laws and influences. Most often, he cannot do the same main activities he had done during his earthly life as the circumstances and priorities in the dimensions of the astral level are completely different from the ones of the physical level. Still, the progress and knowledge that was achieved on various subjects during terrestrial existences is synthesized within his consciousness and can determine the nature of his future reincarnation.

"The alchemist in my example will return in a new reincarnation and will go very quickly through the stages of knowledge he has already achieved in his previous existence. Then, his progress will slow down as he finds himself again in 'unknown territory' that needs exploring. He might need another one or two reincarnations, this assuming that his life goal will always be to obtain spiritual realization by fulfilling the Great Alchemical Work. Destiny, however, has many other vectors of influence that can distract him from the path and delay his success. This is why sometimes even fifteen to twenty lives can pass without him achieving the ultimate aim.

"On the other hand, I benefit from having an extraordinarily long life in a perfectly healthy and balanced physical body and therefore do not have to resume again and again the process of learning and gaining knowledge of every stage of life, starting with childhood and ending with old age. Even more, my consciousness is not subject to the recurrent 'forgetfulness' between two successive reincarnations; and my progress in the alchemical art tends to follow a continuously ascending path. This is why I can obtain the Philosopher's Stone in a few hundred years of study and experimentation while an ordinary man taking the common path of death and rebirth would need at least 3000–4000 years if we assume that he always enjoys optimum circumstances in life, a very favorable destiny, and is particularly inspired and intuitive in his alchemical experiments. These, however, are ideal terms and they rarely come true. Most often, a man needs several tens of thousands, hundreds of thousands or even millions of years to fully evolve spiritually.

"If he would always have, at every reincarnation, the awareness of the cosmic duration of his trip through manifestation, from one level to another, there is no doubt he would fall into a deep despair that would seem unbearable. But, the automated mechanism of forgetfulness that intervenes every time a soul returns to a new existence at the physical level protects him from this terrible anguish.

"Of course, this forgetfulness is necessary and at the same time correlated to the fact that if we were to remember all of our past actions – some of them atrocious – our psyche, still unstable and unprepared to profoundly understand the meaning of all this, would almost surely succumb and our evolution would be compromised for a very long period of time. Also, when we are finally capable of perceiving our previous lives, we are already at a high level of spiritual evolution and that allows us a much superior perspective of our meaning and condition within the Universe. Our vision is then unifying and causes are seen in their global aspect, not just partially."

"Yes, it seems that the advantage of living for a very long time in the physical body is obvious," I admitted. "In a way, the one who is reborn again and again at the physical level is forced to go through the same stages of life and can even be sidetracked from the path he followed a few lives before. This continuous movement of 'up and down' can become tiring, but it is part of our destiny. Even the fact that you have been chosen by your ancestor to carry forward the tradition and thus benefit of a life of approximately 2000 years is also part of your destiny."

"I have often reflected over this myself and there is no doubt it is true. It is clear that some sort of merits I obtained in previous lives facilitated the situation I am in at the present. Still, by virtue of the same cosmic law of destiny, I am almost sure that I had certain ties with this path in my past existences. Usually, smaller or bigger groups of individual souls are almost irresistibly attracted to each other on the screen of life and time due to the fact they are connected by common feelings, experiences, facts or knowledge. That's why a great percentage of the souls that reincarnate meet people during their new life with whom, in one way or another, they have been connected to in other lives. These reciprocal connections are required by virtue of the law of compensating the actions and 'dues' that some have for others. Hence, imagining a possible scenario, I might have been the disciple of an ancient priest that knew this terrible secret of longevity or helped in some way to maintain this special tradition. Still, my hypothesis is not necessarily true as I could have obtained certain spiritual merits leading to the present situation practicing other virtues or religious beliefs than the path I am on now. These aspects remain, for now, shrouded in mystery."

"I know very well that some people have the extraordinary capacity of 'seeing' their previous lives," I said. "I wonder if this signifies some sort of clairvoyance."

"Of course it is clairvoyance," said Elinor. "Such a person has access to a superior level of consciousness that includes a very high dimension of Creation. This dimension refers to the 'recordings' I was telling you about as nothing is ever destroyed without a trace and lost in nothingness."

I wanted to better clarify this aspect.

"Cezar told me about the akashic imprints that are like some sort of huge recording tape, on a subtle level, for everything that happens in the universe," I said. "Does the human consciousness need access to these imprints in order to remember previous existences?"

"The case of being able to visualize past lives is something more than that as it also involves a certain kind of mental control. Of course, this power has its own stages of mastery. If it only manifests sporadically and partially in the beginning, it becomes stable and can even be manifested at will as we progress spiritually. In its superior stages, it can allow us to know, if we wish, the previous lives and the probability of future lives of every human being we know. This is useful in order to understand certain causes from the past that generated some complicated situations in the present. Getting to the root of problems in this way, they can easily and successfully be resolved. I am telling you all this as I too, even if given a special existence, find myself facing many challenges, tendencies or impulses that can avert me from the path I was assigned."

Elinor's last observation conformed with my own conclusions and I added my part.

"I thought it might not be that easy," I said. "After all, a very long life does not spare you at all the effects of your actions; but it gives you the possibility to adjust it 'as you go' without interruptions."

"I use my very long life in order to evolve spiritually," Elinor assented. "Based upon what my ancestor told me as well as what I have experienced myself up to now, I have realized that I practically have no choice. I could, of course, launch other types of activities such as pursuing enormous wealth, but this aspect is completely irrelevant, especially in my case, as I have been bequeathed a fabulous material and financial inheritance. Nevertheless, the majority of people prefer spending almost their entire lifetime – short enough as it is – trying to obtain wealth, luxury and richness. I don't want to sound like a passé philosopher, but you know very well how illusory these material possessions are: what you have now can easily disappear the next moment. In the bitter fight for wealth, the senses go numb; the personality becomes corrupted; and the mind loses its clarity. All of these are traded for the illusory feeling of a thrilling business life or fleeting moments of exaggerated luxury that serve no purpose other than to weaken the spirit. The rich realize this within their inner core but refuse to admit it openly as they would not then know what else they could do with their life outside of their relations, businesses and competition that often destroys and does not stimulate. They would then feel completely exposed, useless to society and disoriented. You can see examples of this in businessmen that have gone bankrupt. They are incapable of relaxing or looking at life from a different perspective other than business, connections and intrigues, even when they are on holiday. I don't know if you've noticed, but this is exactly the reason why many businessmen refuse to take any days off and always justify it by having to sort out issues that cannot be postponed. Their disorientation and inability of understanding anything else in life, except the specific area of business, is the only effect the struggle for money has produced. The situation is truly dramatic for those who are very rich or for some politicians. They like to believe that they live the so called high-life, and once they have had a taste of this luring temptation, it is very hard to let go of it. Their correct perception of reality is then profoundly distorted and their aim in life becomes staying on top. They seek to impress through wealth, connections and financial means, all of which are characteristics that are obviously related to an impure and gross level of consciousness. The fact that they are hiding from themselves is then supported by the ideology of our modern system of culture and education itself which encourages man to believe that there's nothing else beyond these material goals that we all should have in this life. They believe there is no god, no divine spirit, no law of compensation after death, or no reincarnation to make possible this balancing of actions."

"Even more," I added, "these ideas are purposely propagated in order to achieve some vicious goals. This was very clearly presented to me by Cezar when he told me about his meetings with Signore Massini." *

Elinor nodded affirmatively and then continued on with the subject at hand.

"There is a very simple explanation of the materialistic and atheist indoctrination that is supported almost desperately by the structures of power. If people come to realize that the meaning of their existence is completely different than what they think it is, their priorities would change dramatically. For example, if they truly understand what the nature of their actions imply –

---

* See Chapters 3 and 4 of *Transylvania Sunrise* by Radu Cinamar. Massini is a leading Italian Freemason who tried to corrupt Cezar Brad so that his group could gain access to the hidden chamber beneath the Romanian Sphinx.

sometimes during the same lifetime or a future one – they might come to realize that what they are experiencing or will experience is an exact 'replica' of an earlier life. Their mature thinking and the understanding of these aspects would cause them to be more responsible towards their own goals and would stimulate them to be freer in their thinking. This would inevitably lead to a significant change in the distribution of power on the planet as humans would not be so easy to manipulate anymore. The interest in the material level would diminish considerably; therefore, the consumption of goods would decrease and would adapt to the natural necessities as opposed to the excess you see nowadays. Of course, if people buy less and are more interested in the esoteric and spiritual aspects of their life, then payments decrease very rapidly and so do leaders' and rich people's power to control and manipulate via money. A practically new society would emerge based upon real and correct principles. At present, however, this is what is least desired by the occult organizations that lead the destiny of Humankind.

"In reference to this, there are people that claim, full of emphasis and importance, that all ideas regarding the great global conspiracy, the control of the masses and the manipulation of people are just inaccuracies, lacking substance and concrete proof. Unfortunately, these human beings are showing a psychology full of fear and selfishness. Thinking they speak for many others, they are in fact indirectly expressing the anguish and insecurity they sharply feel deep within their being. Still, for those with common sense and correct discernment, the signals received from outside and the way events are unfolding on the global scene are enough to convince them of the slippery slope that humanity is on now and will cause them to act, each according to their own possibilities, so as to give a new direction and new meaning to the destiny of us all. If you look carefully, you will see that this is actually a terrible fight between a few with the supreme power of spiritual knowledge against those who deviated from the path and now seek to attract Humankind towards chaos and ruin."

I knew what he was saying only too well from all of the memorable talks I had with Cezar. I interrupted Elinor, trying to highlight a certain aspect.

"There are many people out there who know these things and lucidly see the state of it all. Still, the majority of them allow the feelings of sadness and depression related to these aspects to engulf them and this is a big mistake. After all, the world we perceive is in a state of continuous motion and transformation. Whatever we do, we cannot stop its fluctuation and instability; but we can direct it towards good and harmony. The restlessness of the world also causes the restlessness of our mind, and this is exactly the situation of those that enter a fight without even seeing it. As if they were blind, they too will suffer the same as the others; but they won't know how to get out of there.

"In my opinion, in order to sort out this painful aspect, we need to change our attitude. Knowing the way the world is, we shouldn't let ourselves be attracted or influenced by the version that it offers as this will cause our suffering. If we manage to look at the world from the outside while still being in it, it means we've solved the issues as far as we are concerned. The more of us who succeed in this, the better it will be for the whole of humanity as such an attitude is deeply spiritual and brings us closer to the truth. I have often talked with Cezar about this aspect. He told me that one of the most efficient methods of being inside and outside the world at the same time is to profoundly understand its governing laws. When you speak about destiny, I've told myself that the correct understanding of its characteristics can spare man of an almost never ending suffering."

"Indeed," responded Elinor. "Most often destiny is associated with suffering; and as you know, this is due to the bad actions committed in the past for which man needs to pay. This basic fact is still unacceptable for the majority of people, but I have explained to you the reasons hidden in their subconscious causing them to choose 'I do what I want; I don't have to account for anything.' After all, it is a matter of consciousness that if they

71

manage to 'put their consciousness to sleep' then they would be spared accounting for the bad things they do and which might make them feel embarrassed and cause discontent. The greater the 'occulting' of their consciousness, the greater their blindness for their actions. Thus, they reach a stage where they cannot discern between virtue and non-virtue anymore. They often claim not to understand what is wrong with lying, stealing, cheating, swindling, counterfeiting, or even resorting to violence as, according to their mentality, 'this is how it is in business' and 'everybody knows it but no one admits it.' This pathetic and almost permanent fight for money, power or fame is senseless in essence; firstly, because all these things don't last; and secondly, because they generate renewed destiny ties that must be 'paid.' The Orient calls this karma. I have no doubts you know very well the meaning of this term which, roughly speaking, refers to the connection between cause and effect.

"Still, karma is a very complex notion. Think for a moment that there are sometimes more causes that determine the same effect. For example, the fact that you came to meet me involved a cumulus of multiple circumstances: you were healthy when it was possible for you to haven fallen seriously ill just the day before; you arrived here safely by car or other mode of transport when you could have had a serious accident on the way; you had the necessary interest to speak to me; you found the right address as you could have gotten lost; and, of course, many other secondary causes that made this meeting possible.

"Even if others consider these aspects to be inconclusive so as to be taken for granted, it is not entirely so as every element has its reason and leads towards something coherent in life. That's why it is not at all by chance the way we act, be it physically with our body or mentally with our thoughts. Each and every one of these ways of manifesting that we have at our disposal automatically generate 'an answer' in our future destiny; namely, our karma. All of these 'answers' build a clear image of our future destiny; predominantly good or bad. Sometimes, when necessary, 'the answer' to a certain kind of action is so fast and obvious that it leaves no doubt in regards to the existence of the universal law of destiny. Nevertheless, many ignore even such clear signals."

"And this despite their suffering," I said. "Everybody wants to be happy and nobody wants to struggle. For this we need to observe the causes leading to happiness and compare them with the causes leading to suffering. It is easy in theory but even this effort proves too much for some."

I was interrupted by Elinor's ringing mobile. After a few replies in English over the phone, he finished the conversation and told me that his Tibetan friend apologized for the delay but had a few difficulties on the way here and had to sort it out. I was also told that he was going to arrive in approximately a half an hour. That made me happy as I thought the meeting was going to be rescheduled, but Elinor told me it concerns a very important circumstance and could not be postponed. He speculated that maybe that was why the lama had some problems that could have prevented him from coming.

"Sometimes there are forces that strongly oppose a certain positive event happening. In practical terms, a change in the causality rapport is what is desired," he explained.

"It means your friend is a spiritual master who knows how to resolve such situations!" I exclaimed.

"Of course. His story is very special indeed," Elinor answered mysteriously. "You will be surprised to find out that there are some connections between you two that, even though indirect, facilitated the present turn of events."

"Very well, " I said. "After all, this is precisely the reason I came here; but before your Tibetan friend arrives, I would like you to tell me how the meeting in Brussels ended. I admit that I am amazed by your story and I still can't completely digest the explanations you gave me. Actually, I think that such information would make others smile incredulously rather than accepting even a small part of what you told me."

"This may be so," said Elinor, "but beyond that they won't

be left with anything valuable. As far as my life is concerned, the truth is too troubling for those with an ordinary understanding. In your case, however, I thought that you have already passed some difficult tests and needed to know more about me."

Having said that, Elinor rose from the armchair and left the living room. After a few seconds, he came back holding a strange object that at first glance resembled an ornamental sculpture. I immediately understood that this was the mysterious object that facilitated colossal longevity. I nervously picked it up and looked at it carefully. It was made out of a metallic cube, and its side of approximately fifteen centimeters looked like a net with a large rhomboid-shaped mesh. Inside this cube and inscribed within it was a sphere made of the same metal. Like the cube, its outer contour was a net but its mesh was smaller. Finally, within the sphere was inscribed a tetrahedron, a perfect representation of a miniature pyramid with the apex pointing upwards.

The tetrahedron was the main element, the central piece of the ensemble. Besides the fact that its surface was opaque, the small pyramid was made out of a different type of metal than the cube and the sphere. For the latter, the metal had reddish reflexes, that resembled copper. I was very surprised by the perfect finish; and even with the matte surface it still created strange lights and shadows between the nets constructing the cube and the sphere.

I asked Elinor what kind of technology had been used in obtaining the metal and to precisely assemble all of the components of the object, but he answered that this information is part of the secret of initiation and cannot be disclosed. Still, he mentioned that the 'hot spot' of the ensemble was the little pyramid, the secret 'heart' that ensures the mysterious influence over the life of the one the object has been built for.

Indeed, the pyramid had a fascinating color that is similar to turquoise that, with every little move, reflected light in the most unexpected ways. I assumed that it happened due to the perfect finish of its surface, but Elinor told me it was actually one of the properties of the mysterious alloy that the pyramid was made of.

The combination of the reddish color of the net that made up the cube and the sphere, combined with that of the turquoise (sometimes going to dark blue) of the pyramid, all in the pale light of the room, was having a strange effect upon my psyche. I felt driven towards dreaming and reverie, but Elinor's voice brought me back to the present.

"Even if it's not tuned to your specific frequency of vibration, the object still creates a certain kind of subtle interaction, particularly with a receptive person. Imagine it as a type of relay or physical intermediary that is very finely tuned to translate certain cosmic energies that the scientists aren't even aware of. That is why its subtle impregnation causes an almost instantaneous specific reaction in the one it is close to. If you, who are not tuned to the object's 'wavelength,' very quickly felt its influence, imagine how I perceive its subtle characteristic action. It's like a strong connection between me and this object that I feel as a very specific and very pleasant vibration in my entire body. It 'nourishes' me and supports me permanently; and what I predominantly feel is a state of perfect balance of all the organism's functions and processes."

I was listening to Elinor while holding the object and turning it on all sides. It was very light considering that all its components were metallic.

"Is the pyramid empty inside?" I asked out of curiosity, trying to find an explanation for the amazing lightness of the ensemble.

Elinor was quiet for a few moments, looking like he could not decide if it was all right to disclose the truth. Lifting my eyes towards him, I thought my question innocent; but I noticed that, without meaning to, I raised a sensitive issue.

"I will tell you," he replied, "that this is the most important secret that needs to be kept; not necessarily in regards to the pyramid's content but the method of obtaining what is inside it."

He paused for a bit to turn the light on and then continued.

"The pyramid is not compact. Its walls are made of an alloy

unknown to humans and inside it, right in the center, is embedded a very special violet crystal.

"The way of obtaining this crystal is the big advantage of the path I'm following as this crystal is the one that personalizes the object. It is what 'attracts' the specific radiation; and at the same time, it encodes the influence of a certain subtle energy of the Universe to the owner's particular frequency of vibration. Without it, the ensemble wouldn't be able to create the effect you now know it does. On the other hand, the crystal on its own can't be of any efficiency without the special interaction it has with the alloy of the pyramid. The whole ensemble 'vibrates' in a very exact way, and the tuning of the frequency is continuously adjusted by the secret alloy. You can even say it possesses a sort of 'intelligence' as it reacts to the slightest energetic changes of the live organism for which both it and the crystal have been personalized through a very secret alchemical methodology. If you place the object on the table and leave it still, you will notice that the alloy keeps on 'moving' or at least creates the sensation of movement."

I was observing this phenomenon in amazement, and I remembered the mysterious material that covered the Great Gallery in the secret location beneath the sphinx in the Bucegi Mountains. Its 'behavior' was similar to the alloy's with the same 'nuances,' the same type of 'intelligent' behavior, and the same kind of special influence over anyone near it. The noticeable difference was that the material in the Great Gallery had an organic component while the alloy that made the pyramid was made of pure metal.

"All the parts of the object are alchemically obtained after very precise recipes," said Elinor. "That includes the violet crystal found in the pyramid, too. That is the most difficult to obtain, but the process is not that long. What is essential is that the one who knows the secret is already a true master of alchemy.

"As a matter of fact, the tradition of the path is only continued through spiritual accomplishment. If the one who possesses the object doesn't achieve perfection in the Great Alchemical Work, he won't have any follower of his own as he won't be capable of making the object or will only be able to make some components of it. He won't be able to obtain the central crystal even if all of the theoretical knowledge of the 'recipe' is available. The reason for this is that he would be missing an essential subtle component that is fundamental for personalizing the object, a quality that is only obtained when accomplished spiritually. No matter his efforts in obtaining the violet crystal; no matter if he repeats the experiment for thousands and thousands of times, he won't be able to personalize the object and it won't have any effect.

"But, exactly because there is this condition, the disciple is given an extremely long life in the physical body so that the maturity and experience he will then achieve contributes to the realization of the Great Alchemical Work. As I've already told you, this is absolutely necessary in order to be fully successful in making the object. The end result is always certified by the superb violet color that the crystal then gets."

"Now I'm more aware of the importance of the path you're following," I said, convinced. "Until now, I couldn't understand the specific way it leads to spiritual realization. Although the master-disciple connection doesn't seem too strong within this tradition, I intuit that in your case it was slightly different. Tell me, have you been helped and supported quite a lot in your search by your ancestor who was also your master? I am asking you this because, as far as I understand, his master left him quite soon after revealing the path."

"That is true, but don't forget that my ancestor spent more than twenty years by the Hindu magician's side, all prior to his initiation. He already knew very many alchemical secrets; and moreover, as he said so himself, the magician left him a small fortune to get on in the world when beginning his 'journey.' It seems there is a tradition on this path whereby the master takes care of the chosen disciple at all levels, including the financial one. Considering that the masters of this spiritual lineage had a perfect knowledge of the alchemical art and were at any time capable of obtaining the Philosopher's Stone, it was very easy for them to make any quantity of precious metals to give to the disciple. Don't think, however, that it was done without any discernment. In such a case, the master's intention would have been incompatible with the perfect and integrated way of acting that an accomplished alchemist manifests. I was significantly helped in this direction by my ancestor. Without exaggerating, I can say that he left me a real treasure. I am not referring to a chest with jewelry and gold coins but very substantial funds in banks plus several pieces of real estate in the main cities of the world."

"Yes, I suspected that," I said. "Still, it is irrelevant as when you are faced with a two-thousand-year-long life, even if you save little but consistently, you can gather a great fortune."

"Logically, you are right; but in reality, things are not quite like that," said Elinor as he smiled slightly. "In order to correctly understand the psychological 'mechanism' of a human being that knows he can live for thousands of years in the physical body, you must first start from different premises and goals that the respective being might have. There are profound transformations taking place, and these cannot and should not be ignored. Paradoxically, the focus is more on the occult aspects of life rather than the concrete, immediate, and material ones that most human are used to.

"The intentions of such a person converge more and more towards self-realization and grace to a specific subtle 'imprint' of this path created over the millennia. The chosen disciple understands fairly quick the purpose as well as the subtleties of his new way of living. Because his social integration starts to become difficult, he is then given the necessary financial resources to easily overcome the obstacles in this direction. These means are not at all offered for his pleasure or desire although you could say that he then has everything he wants. His situation is unusual and that's exactly why it needs to be treated differently."

"Besides the financial help, did your ancestor offer you any spiritual teachings?" I asked.

"It is traditional to this path for the master to retreat from his disciple's side immediately after offering him the final investiture. In my case, the master stayed with me in Brussels for another three weeks after my initiation. We both spent most of the time in his alchemical laboratory which was in the basement of the villa. I was thus initiated in a series of basic procedures and alchemical knowledge in order to help me start my own alchemical experiments. His decision to stay with me for a while longer after my initiation was justified even if it didn't respect the tradition as any path and any method must be adapted to the present social, political and cultural context.

"As far as I'm concerned, I think I was chosen by him mainly due to my stable structure and to the openness and sincerity that is characteristic in me. Maybe my ancestor also intuited other aspects within me.

"Anyway, the specifics of the contemporary world do not allow a long stage of initiation in the occult sciences, especially in regards to the path I am on. The divergent interests, malefic intentions, secret services and advanced technology modify totally the vision of engaging in and then continuing this tradition. Practically speaking, there is an earth to heaven's difference between the two ways we learned alchemy. The circumstances my ancestor lived in around 1500, when he received the initiation in the far-away Indies, and the ones from the end of the last century, around 1970, when I myself got initiated and tutored by him in the alchemical mysteries, are totally incomparable. Plus, I didn't have any previous esoteric knowledge and didn't study the subject at all. Of course, three weeks are too little time to grasp even the basis of the occult sciences; but even so, that period proved very useful in getting an idea about what I needed to know and then realize in my long life. Of great help was the immense library of my ancient ancestor, a collection that contained work and documents of an inestimable value. Not even now can I say that I've finished studying its main volumes. Meanwhile, I too have added to the books that existed then with very important works. Besides, I own another three great libraries in my houses abroad.

"The guiding ideas I had received from my ancestor in those few weeks he stayed by my side formed a sort of 'matrix' that oriented my ulterior activity. Even when his turn of phrase in Romanian was a bit strange, particularly the order of the words, I still managed to understand even the most secret aspect of the practice as where he didn't know the specific terms, my ancestor would turn to French. He told me that he learned Romanian ever since my parents first came to Transylvania. He would do that every time: learn the language of the country his successors chose to live in, mainly to be able to better understand and more efficiently follow the evolution of the members of his genealogical lineage. He never intervened though and remained hidden and unknown to those before me on the main branch but carefully followed and analyzed their lives. He knew fourteen foreign languages and several dialects, a direct result of his world travels. At present, I only speak five foreign languages; but for now, that is enough.

"My ancient relative gave me some essential directions regarding the specific ways of acting in modern society in order to avoid the thorniest issues that could personally concern me. In the last couple of days, he introduced me to very trustworthy people who were former disciples of his. They played an important role that in the following years helped me greatly to take some delicate actions in direct connection to my 'cover' around the world."

Elinor then told me about some very special contacts he had made in the last few years. Among these was the Tibetan lama that announced his arrival that night. He also told me about the emotional parting from his ancestor and revealed some aspects regarding future events happening worldwide. Elinor said that although there are many prophecies and previsions for the times to come, one of these deserves special attention as it is integrated into the 'logic' of cosmic becoming. But at the exact moment he was getting ready to reveal more information about the source of the prophecies and their impact over the consciousness of the people, we heard the door bell. I then had an instantaneous intuition that my meeting with the Tibetan lama was going to have a great importance for my future existence. Even so, the surprise I had when he entered the room surpassed any of my expectations.

In the approximately three hours that I spent in Elinor's company, I found out information that without any doubt would shock any normal being and provoke an inner desire to strongly reject it. These apparently normal reactions would be the direct expression of a sudden break in the rhythm of the routine conceptions and activity of the contemporary man. I consider that I surpassed this major handicap long ago and was therefore open to any challenges in this direction. I already had an important stock of knowledge, explanations and shocking revelations that have mostly been supported by material proof that qualify as highest ranking state secrets.

Even so, the meeting with the Tibetan priest amazed me so much that I needed a few good seconds to get my voice back. My surprise was endless as that was, after all, the first time I was confronted with a reality completely different from the objective reality I knew.

2

THE TIBETAN CONNECTION

Enveloped by an unknown emotion, I got out of the arm-chair and waited to meet this mysterious character. I heard fragments of a conversation in English and then the sounds of the two men's steps as they approached the living room.

The first to enter the room was the Tibetan. He was relatively short, approximately 50 years old, and was wearing a dark blue suit made of a natural fibre, probably cotton. His suit looked a lot like a Chinese uniform but had a much more elegant cut and a modern twist.

I was amazed to notice that even though it was quite cold outside, especially at night, the lama was not wearing anything else over his suit. His eyes were very alive and his look was extremely piercing. Due to the unusual force that the Tibetan was manifesting through his eyes, without leaving the impression of sternness or toughness, I felt a little embarrassed and even inhibited. This aspect, however, proved to be insignificant in the light of what was to follow.

The Secret of a Yidam

After the lama took a few steps into the room, I expected to see Elinor behind him but it was not he who appeared. Instead, there was a being whose presence made me involuntarily shout in surprise. I stood frozen on the spot with my eyes fixed on him, incapable of making any move. Behind the Tibetan was a gigantic man whose head almost touched the ceiling. I think he was taller than two and a half meters. Due to the unusual nature of the creature I witnessed, I feel that it is my responsibility to give some explanations in regards to the "human" status of that being.

His somatic structure seemed to be one of a mature man save for the proportions I have already mentioned. Nevertheless, his aspect was truly "explosive." When I say that, I am referring to the very real meaning of the term that is, of course, meant to be interpreted figuratively. The simple presence of that gigantic being in the room seemed intent on "crushing" me or at least causing me a strong feeling of inner fear.

Trying to control my emotions and reaction, I did not ask any questions. Instead, I took a good look at the giant's face. His hair was black and long below the shoulders, but it was tousled, resembling a terrible mane surrounding his head. His face was adorned with an enormous moustache that accentuated the terrific radiation he emitted. His black eyes seemed to dance in flames and his frowning eyebrows did not foretell anything good. As I was going to see soon, however, the look of that being was his naturally given aspect or his normal existential condition which, by the way, grossly contradicts the way others perceive and understand the presence of those around them.

The yidam was obviously of Asiatic origin with a dry complexion, a tanned face as if he were sunburned, oblique eyes, and a nose that was a little flattened, thus suggesting a possible Tibetan root. His clothes were another point of reference as they were completely unusual: very large trousers made of a very thick black material, a red blouse with large sleeves, a wide belt made of multicolored scarves, and a long yellow cape. Under the folds of the cape, I could see the tips of a pair of huge wooden clogs. This being could very well serve as a signaling beacon.

It was then that I noticed two aspects that confused me even more. The more carefully I looked at him, the more the air surrounding him started to dance, just as it does above the very hot sand in the desert. Trying to focus as much as I could on his outer contours, I had the strange feeling that his contours were dissipating in contact with the air around him. If I focused on the turbulent area, however, the disturbing effect stopped and the contours of the yidam's body became very clear. I was greatly confused by this optical illusion as I could not understand if this was a real being or just an ephemeral apparition. Although I had not said a word up to that moment and had not requested any explanation, the Tibetan lama answered my exact question in perfect English.

"It all depends from what perspective you want to look at this body. If you think of it as the body of an ordinary human being, then you must know it is as real as they come. It has a physical consistency, movements and gestures common to any other human being; but if you try to detect the more subtle aspects of his existence, then your mind will automatically interact with a more profound subtle reality that is the existential foundation of the one before you. If so, your perception of his physical reality will be slightly 'toned down' and your brain will not know how to interpret the strange phenomenon of the vibrating air that surrounds him."

"But...after all, who or what is he?" I dared to ask, timidly.

The Tibetan priest was still standing before me with his hands and forearms together. Although he was looking at me as from far away, I felt certain that he was looking deep into my being. Even so, I did not feel any opposition or discomfort as his ample subtle influence enveloped me. It was calming, relaxing, protective, and understanding.

"It is quite difficult to explain what he is, but I can tell you that in Tibet he is known as a yidam. For now, you can consider him as a reliable companion of the one who invokes him."

"What do you mean by a companion?" I asked, confused.

"A very valuable company, especially through the hardships of life," the lama continued.

I still could not understand. There were too many unanswered questions swarming in my mind. Why do they look this menacing? What can a yidam do? Does he behave like a normal human being? What is his purpose? I practically did not know which of these questions to ask first.

Meanwhile, the lama sat down in the armchair that Elinor had sat in earlier. Elinor remained standing and smiled, slightly leaning on the fireplace. Silently, the yidam moved immediately behind the Tibetan priest's armchair and next to his left shoulder. As the initial surprise lessened and I was returning to an almost normal state of mind, I noticed another disturbing aspect attributable to the yidam's presence. The room was filled with a characteristic smell that I have identified with ambergris; but at times I could also feel vague wafts of myrrh that gave the space we were in a certain sacredness. Initially, I thought Elinor was burning incense, but I realized there was no basis for my assumption as there was no smoke in the room and the smell was very delicate and pure. When the yidam moved behind the armchair that the lama sat in, I knew he was the source of the sublime smell that was radiating throughout the room. When the yidam passed very close to me, I felt how that smell was wafting from him. I confess that, for a second, I wondered if he had used some expensive brand of perfume. Embarrassed by such a ridiculous assumption, I immediately realized that no matter how delicate and valuable a commercial perfume might be, it could never equal the fragrant emanations of a sacred being; and I was starting to suspect that the yidam was exactly that.

"From a Western point of view, the presence of a yidam is not only disturbing, it is also completely incomprehensible," the lama said. "I will give you some explanation though regarding this matter because I have considered it would be appropriate to do so the moment I decided you were able to see a yidam."

I was just sitting down, but upon hearing the lama's last words, I froze before finally speaking.

"I'm afraid I don't understand. Actually, I don't understand anything anymore. From what you've said I can conclude that seeing a yidam is a privilege; or better said, a gift, an act of grace."

I was honestly surprised and slightly skeptical.

"It's more of a personal choice that depends upon the person we are meeting and what we wish to realize. I am talking now about matters that are nowhere near the conceivable mental attitude of a normal human being. This is exactly why ordinary humans cannot see a yidam," the lama added as he pointed to the giant being behind him. "This is not due to their incapacity, however, but to the yidam's will; and he can remain completely invisible to other people."

"And despite all this, I will still be able to see him?" I asked in amazement.

"Yes, you will see him as you see him now, but the others will not notice his presence. For them, he basically does not exist. I repeat, this is a direct result of the yidam's will. Sometimes, as it is now, it is necessary for his body to be perceived by you too as Elinor and him are already old acquaintances," he said smiling.

Only then did I realize that Elinor did not react in any way when the giant entered his house.

"OK, but why all this?" I wanted to know.

The lama tilted his head slightly forwards.

"This is not the purpose of the meeting I requested and I do not want to digress too much. Nonetheless, I will give you some details about the mysteries of a yidam as it is necessary that your understanding of these matters is as correct as possible. This will helps us later in what we have to do."

The lama stopped for a moment and closed his eyes. Immediately afterwards, he opened them. Fastening his eyes on me, he started to talk.

"In Tibet, there is a certain stage of spiritual practice when the disciple, under the close supervision of his master, starts the technique that allows the creation of a yidam."

I was not even blinking anymore.

"Did you just say 'to create a yidam'?" I asked.

The procedure is very complicated and difficult to carry

out," the lama continued without paying attention to my perplexity. "It requires special accuracy in building a colored sand mandala; and afterwards, the disciple must make consistent efforts to become successful in certain mental focusing and visualization techniques. All of these must be done in complete isolation and on a very severe diet. Add to this the low air temperature in the mountains, which often dips below zero, and you will understand why this spiritual stage of the aspirant's life can sometimes last for two years or more. Besides, the ones who deserve to receive this initiation from their master and manage to fulfill such a spiritual practice are relatively few. Many give up along the way or are just not capable of understanding some fundamental subtle aspects that would ensure their complete success.

"Even after creating a yidam, who then becomes an entity with a physical aspect and form — the same as you and me — the issue is still suspended and the disciple needs to solve it. He needs to understand the real nature of the yidam and what characteristics he has. Out of those who succeeded in creating a yidam, some decide for him to accompany them their entire life, always guiding them in difficult situations and pointing them towards higher and higher levels of spiritual progress. Others, who are very few in number, are able to infer the nature of the yidam from the beginning. Even so, the nature of a yidam is still illusory; and thus they remain focused in a very profound meditation that transcends even this very sophisticated illusion."

"And what is the nature of a yidam?" I asked impatiently.

I was watching the gigantic being behind the priest with fascination and respect but also a little fear. Although I was starting to get used to his presence, his frightening look still made me shiver.

"In essence, the nature of a yidam is purely mental," the lama responded. "Irrespective of the complicated stages that the creation of a yidam involves, its essence is mental. The disciple then proves his abilities of mental focus and efficient control of the mind. I think it is already no mystery to you that, in reality, it is the mind which creates the entire phenomenal world that is perceived by man from moment to moment. The mind carries his daily activities. It is then up to the disciple as to whether he will finally realize the illusory nature of this formidable mental force that he possesses or whether he will get attached to it and remain chained in the illusion that surrounds him.

"In fewer words, a yidam is the quintessence of the mental energy of the one who evokes and creates it, coming from the profound particularities of his personality and subconscious. That is why yidams are not identical but express different behavioral attitudes. Some yidams belong to the terrible entities category while some belong to the gentle entities one. Some are spiritual guides, and there are many more categories as well. The one in this room is of the terrible category but do not let that fool you and make you believe he is associated with violence or destruction."

"His looks contribute greatly to this impression," I said.

"It is true," said the lama as he smiled, "but think that every yidam, according to the category he belongs to, has a certain and precise meaning to fulfill next to the one who created him."

I intervened in order to voice a spontaneous thought.

"The idea I have about him is to identify him more with some of the djinns or genies of the Arabian Nights tales who, after being released from a bottle or amphora, fulfill the wishes of their liberator," I said, slightly amused.

"You did not understand the substratum lying behind the existence of a yidam," the lama continued. "In Arabic magic and occultism, such djinns exist indeed. They are, in fact, astral entities that are not too elevated. Most commonly known as genies, they have some powers which allow them to fulfill some of the wishes of the human being who invokes them. Do not forget, however, that these acts are always based upon a mutual pact or understanding that is tacitly agreed with by both sides. A yidam is a physical creation that is touchable, and his relationship with the one he accompanies is of a total different nature than those magical pacts. It is true, however, that before being able to materialize or even speak, a yidam goes through some intermediary stages that start with sporadic apparitions that are almost immaterial until he finally takes his definite physical shape and consistency. He then apparently becomes a person like any other, but keep in mind that a yidam always has some of the characteristics of the one who created him."

"So," I said, "I understand that he is a purely mental creation. The Western mind finds it difficult to cope with the idea that the relatively abstract, subtle and intangible aspects of the mind can create a physical form. If I was not here and seeing what I'm seeing, I myself would probably not adhere to such an idea."

"It is a pointless limitation that got imposed due to the habit of believing what you are told," said the lama. "In reality, things are much more nuanced. A yidam 'condenses' out of the very subtle matter of the superior mental levels of the one who practices this complex technique. Hence, even if he finally has a physical body, the matter he's made of has different characteristics from the typical physical body, it not being so rigid. This is why, depending on what is needed, a yidam can remain completely invisible for those he does not wish to show himself to and at the same time allow others to see him. Anyway, I think you realize what it would mean if he would allow everyone to see him walking around town."

The lama smiled suggestively as he completed this last statement. Elinor, who until then had remained silent on one side of the room, now intervened.

"Because his structure is special, he can become invisible and remain penetrable to touch at the same time, like a live hologram. We are talking about a conscious directing of the vibrating matter that makes up his being. As this capacity is exclusively related to the exertion of mental control and because the yidam is a mental emanation of the one who created him, this adjustment of the frequency of vibration of matter is only obvious."

Although I understood what was said, I was still confused by the seemingly unnatural circumstances at work.

"We are here and we talk about him," I said as I pointed to the yidam, "like he is some sort of exhibit being analyzed under a microscope. This being hasn't said a word up to now; didn't voice any opinion. It almost looks like he is an accessory."

"It is a profoundly mistaken impression," the lama explained patiently. "The moment I told you that his nature is mental but still elevated, you should have realized that his purpose is much subtler than the one you imagine. In the beginning, I told you that he is a companion or attendant in order to have a starting point and not shock your power of understanding too much. I then made some important specifications among which was one that a yidam guides the one who created him towards superior stages of spiritual practice. Not only is he not just decorative, but he even becomes a sort of spiritual master for the disciple that he takes care of for the rest of his life.

"Here appears the following dilemma: if the yidam is created by a human being, how is it possible for him to become that being's spiritual master? This apparent problem can be solved if you understand that the yidam represents a sort of interface between the superior mental structures and the physical plane in which the one who created him exists. The subtle aspect of this relationship, somehow symbiotic, is the attachment the disciple may have or develop for his yidam. Being a mental creation, even if belonging to a superior world, it is still ephemeral and can only lead the disciple up to a certain stage of spiritual progress."

Here the lama took a short break. As soon as he did, the atmosphere in the room changed almost suddenly and became strongly ionized, smelling like a forest before a storm. The attitude of the yidam was even statelier and his eyes were shooting fire at me. After a short while and without making any gesture, the lama resumed his explanation.

"He (the yidam) just told me that at a certain level of your mental structure, there are certain tensions of which you are not aware of but that they will disappear soon. They are only the result of your trying to understand and assimilate a large amount of unusual information as soon as possible. Unfortunately, time does not allow us to postpone at all the purpose for which we all gathered here; but at the same time, I wouldn't want you to be left with certain unclear aspects that might generate bigger problems later."

I felt like I was being bombarded from all directions by unexplainable phenomena.

"I didn't hear any word from him," I said slightly irritated.

"You couldn't have anyway," the lama responded. "A yidam only speaks to the one who created him or in his presence, but communication with words is not absolutely necessary. Most often it is done telepathically. Many disciples waive the last part of the technique where the yidam gets a voice as it requires an extra effort and is not absolutely necessary. However, it is correct and safe for the yidam to be also capable of speaking to the disciple as at certain times he cannot have the certainty of the telepathic communication between him and the yidam and thus can confuse his own ideas with the yidam's. Have no doubts, the yidam you see here can speak; but if you heard him, you would have another shock for sure. The voice of a yidam, especially when he belongs to the formidable entities category, is almost paralyzing. This is not necessarily because of its volume but mainly due to its specific frequency being very strange to the human ear. Plus, as I already told you, he only speaks to the one who created him. If you wish, however, I can ask him to address you telepathically so that you have at least an approximate idea of how his voice sounds in reality."

The lama was waiting for my approval which I offered without any reservation. Although excited at the thought of such a new experience for me, I confusedly felt that the physical world that we all usually consider stable and safe had now lost quite a bit of its consistency, but I could not pinpoint the cause of my feeling. Later, objectively analyzing those very special moments, I realized that although the beings and objects in the living room belonged to this world, they were equally transcending it as well. Elinor was practically "immortal" compared to the average life of an ordinary human, and the object facilitating this extraordinary condition was made out of substances that had no correspondence in this world. The Tibetan priest was also a very mysterious character and my intuition told me he possessed explosive secrets. The yidam was an overwhelming presence that best embodied the connection with other worlds. In these circumstances, I had to adapt to make full use of all my powers and capacities of understanding.

The important issue here is that because my brain was recording this bizarre information as coming to me externally, from the outside, coupled with the fact that the reality of these beings and objects were not overlapping with the common concept of daily life, a dream state was starting to generate in my mind. In fact, this was only an extreme solution of my brain in order to cope with the quandary it was in. In the beginning, I was tempted to distrust the yidam's observation; but later, I was convinced that he was perfectly right and that his power of insight at a mental level was remarkable.

On the other hand, from an occult point of view, everything was completely explainable. It is known how notably influential a wave form can be when it is manifested through the use of certain objects in order to create a magical atmosphere. This is exactly why certain props as well as special diagrams and gestures are resorted to during rituals. All of these are used in order to facilitate a "breach" of the separation between levels which is nothing else but a "bridge" between them. The energy of the one doing the magic ritual and the supporting elements that facilitate the orientation of this energy in the desired direction are the basis of any occult action. The being, as well as all the objects used, become genuine relays of caption and manifestation of certain energies belonging to the subtle planes of Creation.

Although we were nowhere close to being involved in a magical proceeding, the principle of the relay of force and of the energy between levels was applying, even if only because of who and what was present. For example, the subtle energetic field of the strange object that prolonged life certainly played its part in the space-time distortion that was happening in the room. The auras of the other three beings were also a major influence in this direction and such that my own aura was then somehow infused with these unusual vibrations that powerfully reverberated in my consciousness.

The dream state I had entered was now suddenly invaded by a sort of voice that resembled a thunder rumble more than anything else. Although I could not actually understand the words, the idea that was transmitted was very clear. The yidam was telling me that in order to ease and relax my mental tension, he had modified the ambiance of the room, cooling it down and infusing it with vitality. My head resounded with the rumbling of his words which were reminiscent of but not really like thunder from a storm. I was trying to find an analogy, but in reality, the impression was much more complex.

Pretty dazed, I managed to thank the yidam telepathically. Suddenly, my mind and the living room became overwhelmingly quiet. There was not a sound nor movement, just a frozen silence. Peering with my eyes half ajar, the environment seemed somehow unreal. It was almost to the point where I could not feel the contours of my body. Contrary to my expectations, however, the wonderful state of relaxation that enveloped me did not make me lethargic or induce sleepiness. Instead, it made me more lucid and capable of understanding what was happening with and within myself during every moment that passed. In less than three minutes, I felt so good that I did not wish for anything else other than to remain in that very comfortable state. Intuitively, I realized that the Tibetan lama and the yidam were offering me this wonderful help so that I could overcome a certain mental blockage.

Just prior to this new state of mind, my defense mechanism of the "ego fortress" was very actively trying to generate a state of anguish and uncertainty in order to make me leave the room.

Now, however, I felt an intense joy and was full of warmth and affection for being around those special people as I faced this completely extraordinary situation.

After having retraced with clarity the sequence of events, discussions and inner emotions that I lived during those days, I now realize that only very few people will be willing to accept and sympathize with my experiences, even partially. In such an instance, the main issue seems to be that what I present greatly exceeds the common knowledge and conceptions about life and its hidden mysteries. I said to myself then that I can either reveal the realities I have lived during the days that followed or simply maintain silence. If I choose the latter, however, how could I possibly fulfill the recommendation I was given by the goddess I was soon to meet, Machandi, who advised me to make known to the world all the truths I have live through? How could I still contribute, even to a small extent, to the occult knowledge of Man, a knowledge that is a totally different kind from the superficial one that is experienced within the society?

If it were only one or another of the aforementioned propositions I was faced with then maybe I would not have bothered to describe what had happened. There was, however, an entire series of moving facts and revelations that placed me, in a complicated and at the same time exciting game of destiny, in key-situations that cannot bear comparison to normal circumstances of daily life. Surely, all these circumstances have a very precise meaning and are integrated into a much more complex ensemble than what was only partially revealed to me. On the other hand, I clearly felt that I was constantly supported and helped to successfully pass all the tests I was confronted with in this last period of my life.

I believe that each one of us has a very well determined place in the society we live in, but this does not necessarily refer to our integration into economic, political or cultural life. Nor does it refer to the idea of personal career, fame, wealth, riches, family or material gain. This role comprises a much deeper dimension of our existence; and without it, life looks dull and pointless even if it apparently has a certain attraction and exterior shine. Riches and fame are not only transient; they not durable. At most, they manage to perturb our correct understanding of the world we live in because they are tempting and illusory. Man needs something more than money, public recognition, success in business or ephemeral pleasures. If this were truly Man's meaning in this world, as soon as he would achieve all these things, they should never disappear. Or, the simple fact that they are as illusory as Fata Morgana shows that the material goals of our life are nothing else but a deceiving game that eventually exhausts a being.

The tumult of my later states of experience, the people I have met and the events I have participated in show me that I am on the good and luminous path of spiritual evolution. This generates a comforting feeling and an inner joy in me that accompany me always, being fully convinced that I am supported and helped to progress on the path of knowledge. I now know precisely where I need to look without being allured by false temptations.

I had the extraordinary chance of meeting remarkable beings who taught and initiated me in some esoteric aspects of life, thus opening a completely new horizon over my life's understanding and integration. When I have been confronted with certain conceptual difficulties or certain disturbing facts and realities, I have always been helped to successfully overcome them. In the Projection Room in the Bucegi Mountains, with Elinor's revelations and especially in the presence of the yidam, I have always received the needed help in order to successfully cope with those hiatus moments of my consciousness.

The events I am describing here, however, involved a harsher reality due to the frequency of the events. During the very pleasant state I was experiencing; and then due to the combined subtle action of both the Tibetan priest and the yidam, I was convinced that I had overcome these blockages and that I was ready to bear the eventual coming surprises much more easily.

At the same time, I was amazed by the powers the yidam had manifested towards me. I asked the Tibetan priest for further explanations in regards to this.

"What impressed you were actually simple acts that a yidam can easily realize. Yet, compared to the limited capacities of the human being, these accomplishments seem special. In fact, the powers of a yidam are much grander as he is capable of controlling certain specific energies of the Universe. A yidam must often look out for the physical and psychic integrity of a disciple. It is one of the undertaken responsibilities of a yidam to guide a disciple towards the final liberation in perfect safety. For the most part, a yidam's paranormal interventions are done in order to protect a disciple from being attacked by certain demonic entities or from the malefic influences he is confronted with during his spiritual practice. Such situations mostly appear in the area of Tibet which is particularly known for such manifestations. The mountainous areas, the valleys or the great expanses of plateaus are the main territories of influence of diverse subtle entities that are not always propitious to those that invade their land. They are capable of terrible action in the physical plane that can even claim the life of a disciple. These are some of the situations when a yidam is of great help.

"Of course, one's first intent is to obtain the benevolence of the subtle entity that governs the area where a disciple decides to settle down for a while in order to realize certain spiritual activities and practices. If not, the respective spirit could feel offended and insulted that he is not being given the required attention as the master of the place. Usually, this 'softening' of the spirits is achieved by means of simple rituals where the reasons and the durations of the stay are presented. In order to increase the probability of success, it is common to offer a gift such as food or certain objects that are traditionally consecrated for such actions. If they are pleasing to the respective entity and are accepted, their essential subtle energy is then taken by the spirit while the material offerings are either given to other people or buried in a clean soil. If the entity refuses to collaborate, which is usually manifested as visible and averse exterior phenomena such as terrible storms, threatening lighting, stone avalanches or even harm being brought to the applicant, then the yidam intervenes and starts a 'fight' with that entity. This confrontation can be very short if the difference in powers between the two is very big. On the other hand, if the powers of the yidam and the respective astral entity are close, the conflict can be long and tiring. During all of these, the disciple retreats from the scene of the fight; and if the situation become uncertain, he then tries to help the yidam through the means of certain spiritual practices he knows, most often invoking the additional help of other subtle entities."

"The situations you are describing seem like they are taken out of fairy tales or legends," I stated. "I wonder if there is truly such a reality of terrible confrontations between fantasy creatures. Are these kinds of fights happening in the physical plane?" I asked, curious to know.

"Know that they are much more real than you could ever imagine," the lama answered. "If you can't see it, it doesn't mean it doesn't exist. People nowadays are 'blind' towards these subtle realities as they are very conceited and indoctrinated by materialistic ideology. That is why, even when faced with indubitable evidence of the existence of other levels being manifested, they either refuse to admit it or have a most lamentable psychic breakdown.

"In the subtle planes, such as the astral plane for example, the shapes and colors have a very large spectre of manifestation. That's why many of the entities belonging to this dimension of Creation correspond only vaguely to our representations of them in the physical plane but come very close to the so called fabulous beings described in fairy tales, myths and legends. And, in certain very special circumstances, they can even materialize in the physical plane. Besides, this is a choice for the yidam and the respective entity and occurs only when all other possibilities of fighting and attacking in the subtle planes of existence have been exhausted. In such a case, their manifestation in the physical plane is destructive and the disciple must make sure that he hides very well. Although there are very rare cases when a yidam loses such a battle, the fight usually ends before either of the two is killed, but there are also more dramatic cases."

As I contemplated the giant and silent yidam that was in the same room with us, a question gradually crystallized in my mind.

"Is he the yidam you created all by yourself?" I finally dared to ask.

The lama did not answer me straight away. I was thinking that my question was inappropriate, and I was just getting ready to apologize when he spoke in a neutral tone of voice.

"No. As it stands, the situation is more complicated. It is good, however, that the discussion reached this point as it is connected to the purpose of our meeting. Actually, I myself am a sort of intermediary who needs to fulfill a certain mission as far as you're concerned. Be at peace. It is all positive; however, I can't reveal more than is absolutely necessary right now."

I was wondering how limited "necessary" was as I had been there for almost four hours but still had no idea why I had come. I then realized that although we had been talking for quite a while, I did not even know the name of the Tibetan.

Repa Sundhi

Somehow frustrated by this unusual situation, I expressed my perplexities which seemed justified to me. The lama apologized for not introducing himself as yet. He then told me that he had chosen to give me certain explanations related to the presence of the yidam first as this had consumed all of my attention.

I found out that the Tibetan priest was named Repa Sundhi; that he was born in Tibet but left it after the invasion of the Chinese in 1956 as, at that time, he played an important role in the royal palace of Lhasa. He travelled for a while through several countries on diplomatic missions but eventually settled down in the capital of China, at that time named Peking.

"Still, something is unclear," I said. "I understood that you left Tibet because of the Chinese, and now you are telling me you settled in China."

Repa Sundhi had asked me to give up the formalities and call him by his name. Besides, the age difference between us was not great, but this fact created another dilemma for me. According to his narration, he was active in the capital of Tibet in 1956 which implied him being at least 30-35 years old at that time. His present looks, however, were that of a 50-year-old man. There was a difference of approximately four decades that was not justified.

"We would have gotten here anyway, to this delicate point in or talks," he said. "I am glad that Elinor spoke to you about his secret as this will make you more inclined to easily accept some of the revelations I'm about to make to you."

The lama smiled slightly as he watched the strange object that was on the table.

"I have to tell you," he continued, "that from the beginning I did not belong to the same traditional spiritual path that Elinor follows although I know it very well. In order to understand what I do in the world and what are the goals I pursue, you would need to know some occult aspects first; but we do not now have the time for me to reveal such information. What I can tell you, however, is that I most often fulfill the role of a messenger while at the same time contribute to the successful carrying out of the transmitted message."

"What kind of emissary?" I asked, paying a lot of attention to the discussion. "And what sort of message is this about?"

"Don't think of these messages as letters or something that can be verbally transmitted to someone," the lama replied. Rather, the respective 'messages' can be integrated into certain kinds of spiritual missions in various areas of the world.

In relation to this, you must know that time doesn't affect me almost at all. In certain people, their level of consciousness allows them to act in such a way that they attract to their aura a certain type of cosmic energy, an energy that brings youth. Additionally, there is also a secret concoction of very rare mountainous plants and herbs which contributes to this effect, but I'll stop my explanations here."

I almost did not know what to say anymore. This was going to be an unforgettable evening for sure! I then again asked Repa Sundhi who it is that sends him on such missions.

"The problem is complex," he answered. "In order to correctly understand its subtleties, you would need a strong background of esoteric knowledge, both from an ideological and practical point of view. The one who is initiated in the mysteries of occultism knows very well that Humankind is not left to its own devices. If it were so, it is possible that the negative karma of the earth would have long ago tipped the scale towards destruction. There are though, hierarchically speaking, worlds and civilizations that are meant to maintain, as much as it is possible without interfering with the free will of people, a certain balance for the entire planet. These are very delicate, complex and difficult to understand aspects of reality. On the one hand, this is due to the fact that the direction of science and humanity's conception of the universe is still too deeply materialistic. On the other hand, there are certain occult interests throughout this world which are very strong and are not at all oriented towards positive goals."

"What kind of worlds and civilizations are you talking about? Extraterrestrial ones?" I asked, careful not to enter a slippery or unsafe subject.

The lama became serious and his voice stronger.

"What is the basis of your surprise and perplexity? Have you not already been faced with inexorable evidence in this direction? Have you not been granted access to places where few human beings are allowed at the present? Reality can be disturbing and unbelievable at first sight, but it doesn't mean it doesn't exist. The craze of 'alien invasion' and the mass manipulation that has been systematically going on for the last decades has largely succeeded to discredit this subject in the eyes and minds of many people; however, I hope you are not amongst them. It would be sad, too; especially that you now have knowledge of so much ultra secret information in this field."

I humbly accepted his reproof. In fact, my intention has not been that of denying the existence of other civilizations in the Universe that are much more developed than the human civilization but of expressing my doubt that they could have a positive influence towards the welfare of humanity. In my opinion, to believe or not to believe there are super developed civilizations in this Universe is juvenile, and this is pretty much the level on which such controversies unfold. I am referring to the arguments between some scientists, world politicians and certain UFO supporters or those who present indubitable evidence on the subject. All politicians, and not just them, stubbornly deny the presence of these worlds and seek to prove that they do not in fact exist. This extremely conceited and limited idea that we are alone in the universe, however, is based upon well defined interests concerning total control over Humankind.

Most problems come from Christians as the influence of the church, and the Catholic one in particular, is still quite strong throughout the world. For example, if believers were told by the Pope that other beings also exist in the universe, some much more technologically advanced than humans — and were brought clear proof of this – this would almost certainly give rise to a profound conceptual crisis among the masses. Revealing evidence and contacts with other civilizations would irremediably lead to a dramatic decline of the influence and power of manipulation over humanity as humans would then have other options open to themselves that would be oriented towards different horizons from the one that had been imposed until then. The problem is much more complex, however, and is not limited to just these aspects.

I was already quite familiar with this subject. Even further, I had the opportunity to see in person the incredible technologies in the Projection Room and convince myself of the existence of other civilizations in our Galaxy by watching the synthesis of some holographic projections. Although I was convinced that the great ensemble in the Bucegi Mountains represented the work of an ancient extraterrestrial civilization, Cezar never confirmed it, not even after he revealed to me a great deal of the secret elements of the Great Expedition he participated in. Hence, from this point of view, the mystery was still hidden to me.

I reacted superficially to the information Repa Sundhi was offering me, probably from a primitive ideological reflex that it is very unlikely that Humankind is being watched over by more advanced civilizations. At the same time, I was aware that I had no solid support for this thought.

"On the other hand," the lama continued to explain, "I didn't say I am talking about a terrestrial civilization. I said there are very advanced beings that overlook the well being of humanity. Their powers and capacities are beyond anything you could think of right now."

"Well, where are they?" I asked in genuine astonishment. "Where do they live? Are they among us?"

Repa Sundhi continued to explain, unperturbed.

"Their technological and spiritual progress is so great that it allows the members of that civilization to change, like flicking a switch, the frequency of vibration of matter, when they wish to do so. In a way, it is similar to how a yidam acts, but when necessary, they can change the vibration level of their entire civilization by switching from the physical plane to the astral one and back. However, in order to avoid unwanted contact with the present human civilization, which is impure and gross, they are now in a very special and secret area of which only rumors and hypotheses are known. For the most part, this situation lasted until the great discovery in the Bucegi Mountains was made a little over a year ago."

I kept silent but mentally asked a question with intensity. Repa Sundhi answered immediately.

"Yes, Cezar Brad knows the truth about the respective civilization and the Bucegi location, but he has not been allowed yet to say anything about it after the commando team came back from the Great Expedition, not even to the Romanian or American authorities. At some point during the time spent in the main tunnel, something happened that only Cezar was witness to. The other members of the team did not have access to it. In fact, they do not even know what happened." *

"This means you know Cezar well," I said enthusiastically. "He also told me quite a bit about his grandiose adventure, but some things he didn't share. He told me that he is not yet permitted to, but I think he referred exactly to what you spoke about. I cannot help but wonder though how you got to know Cezar so well that he talked to you about these very secret aspects. He never told me about you."

The lama smiled enigmatically and then began to speak.

"Oh, but he did speak to you about me, but neither you nor he inferred the truth at that time. It was only after he made the great discovery in the Bucegi mountains, during a very special conjuncture that I created, that he was able to meet me again. I am a very old friend of his; and now, the favorable game of destiny has made it such that you are now able to find out certain information that is very secret."

I was trying very hard to identify Repa Sundhi from the information that Cezar had given me, but I did not seem to get any results.

Looking at me kindly, the lama eventually spoke.

"I closely took care of the education and spiritual training of Cezar Brad who is a very evolved being. I cultivated his exceptional abilities and oriented him in a direction that can never fail."

Here the Tibetan stopped for a moment, giving me a last chance to identify him. From the depth of my memories, an

---

* See Chapter 5 of *Transylvanian Sunrise* by Radu Cinamar for further information.

intuition was more and more coming to light. The lama then spoke with much modesty.

"I am Doctor Xien," was all he said.

I was taken aback, not knowing what to believe anymore. Cezar had spoken very little about doctor Xien but always very considerately and affectionately. In a way, I could infer that the Tibetan lama was like a spiritual master during the communist period when he guided Cezar for several years in the secret base near B... Immediately after the 1989 Revolution, however, he suddenly disappeared without anyone knowing anything about it. Neither he nor his assistant left any trace or evidence of their disappearance. Cezar told me that when they contacted the Chinese authorities to inform them of the situation, the Chinese initially had a negative reaction and accused the Romanian secret services of the death of the two. A little while after, however, the whole affair was inexplicably forgotten without any explanations and without the mystery ever being solved. I thought that Cezar, due to his special capacities, knew at least part of the truth but did not want to reveal it to me.

"It is very true that he tried to find me through certain occult ways," the lama said, "but by then he hadn't developed these powers to the point where he was able to suppress certain subtle protection barriers that I manifest in such cases. This protection is justified by the necessity of acting as freely as possible in order to fulfill my spiritual mission while still roughly respecting the 'norms' of modern society."

"Nevertheless, I don't understand what the specifics of your actions throughout the world are," I said to Repa Sundhi. "I gathered that you spent many years in Romania as a Chinese special attaché for paranormal matters. Was that your mission?"

"There are several directions or missions that I fulfill simultaneously, but they are all somehow correlated and this means that they have a common denominator. In order to solve it all efficiently, I have to make certain contacts with people who are involved in one way or another in those situations. This requires that I travel to different places on the globe. Thus, saying I always stay in the same place is an improper turn of phrase. In reality, I travel to many locations in the countries where I have already established contacts. This does not happen, however, in the classical way you are thinking about. I am revealing this secret to you so you can infer that there are many other possibilities that some beings have at their disposal that are beyond the ordinary means a common human being uses to run his daily activities. I am referring to abilities which, according to the standards of present day Humankind, are of a paranormal nature and are used in order to act efficiently.[*]

"You can understand my 'disappearance' from Romania fifteen years ago. An important stage had finished and my presence there was simply not necessary anymore. As events unfolded, it was proven that my assessment was true and Cezar lived up to my expectations. Everything that happened afterwards, including the great discovery in the Bucegi Mountains, is part of a very complex plan, a multidimensional one, of which there is no need to talk to you about at this time. However, with the passing of time, you will be able to understand more and more detailed fragments of this grandiose action that involves the whole planet and in which you play your own role. The accomplishment of this great project concerning the Earth is a combined effort of several very evolved beings, some of them belonging to other planes of manifestation, as you will soon see for yourself."

I was amazed by what I was hearing, but at the same time, I intensely felt the desire to be of use and contribute, as much as I was able, to the realization of this plan. I then wanted to find out more information about the way Repa Sundhi acted in the world.

"The majority of connections I nurture and have access to are at a governmental level," the lama continued. "Although there are many people in this world fighting against good, there are by all means also people with a pure consciousness who wish to be of use to the nation they belong to and even the entirety

---

[*] See references in Chapters 1, 2 & 3 of *Transylvanian Sunrise* by Radu Cinamar.

of humanity. The higher their roles and responsibility in the governments of the world's powers, the more important is their influence. An example is my connection to certain members of the Chinese government. They have facilitated many of my beneficial interventions, and at the same time, they covered certain strange events that could not be explained. These connections are then transmitted and diversified from one generation to another, but these are not my only contacts.

"An important role is played by people who possess strong magnetic powers as well as exceptional abilities provided, of course, that they are beneficially oriented. During the times to come, these people are going to be capable of polarizing many others around them, pointing in the correct direction so that others can understand the critical situation of Humankind in a way that they can and must efficiently act to deeply transform it. It is good to know that Cezar Brad, due to his discreet but well integrated interventions, managed to greatly balance the forces in Romania.

"Everything always needs to be judged from a more subtle point of view than just the physical aspects. An influence is so much stronger when it is first initiated in a subtle causal plane. Only then will it materialize in the physical plane, but the complex manner of its combined effects will be understood by just a few people. Cezar already has the ability to act in this way, but you need to fully understand that in order to have such a capability, the intention of the respective being needs to be very pure."

As Repa Sundhi told me all of these things, my feeling was one of profound gratitude for his wisdom and the kindness he was showing me. Although I only knew him for a little while, I could notice striking similarities in my discussion with explanations I got from Cezar during the last couple of years. It was not too hard to imagine that Repa Sundhi often spoke to Cezar as a master would to his disciple, clarifying many aspects of life and patiently directing him on the path of goodness and righteousness.

I felt wonderful and any previous feeling of anguish or irritation disappeared like magic. I was willing to find out as many things as possible in regards to how I could complete my knowledge and refine my ways of acting. The lama then gave me an explanation that in the beginning seemed surprising.

"One of the very important aspects you need to be aware of regarding knowledge is that all that beings live and feel during their lives becomes experience for the other beings in the universe. The essential element is that it happens independently from space and time. When you achieve the ability to tune into this field of existence that transcends space and time, you practically have access to all 'recordings' and that includes all that has ever happened and will ever happen."

"Amazing!" I said delighted. "Just tonight, Elinor spoke to me about the subtle 'recordings' of manifestation but in connection with previous lives. It's true he didn't tell me too many details, but I gather he was referring to the same aspect you are talking to me about now."

At that moment, Elinor felt it necessary to intervene in order to further clarify things.

"I told him that the power to see previous lives, his or of any other being, is based upon the access by consciousness to a supra temporal plane of existence where accurate recordings exist of any type of action that has ever happened in the phenomenal world," Elinor said, addressing Repa Sundhi. "It is like a 'recording tape' of the Universe."

"Perfectly true," the lama assented seriously. "The access to these precise traces left by any being during its passage through manifestation can help you, in a way, benefit from what we could call 'the experience of the Universe.' It is very important that this is very well understood. After all, any being within Creation is faced with two opposing fundamental existential states: the state of ignorance and the state of knowledge.

"When I refer to ignorance, I mean that the respective being does not know almost any of the essential laws of the universe it lives in. That's why ignorance makes man live only partially, fragmented and isolated in a very limited realm of existence. Metaphorically speaking, he is living in a very small cage without even being aware of it.

"On the other hand, knowledge is power. And I'm not talking here about a theoretical scientific knowledge or what is generally labelled as worldly knowledge but rather what makes up universal knowledge. This is infinitely richer and more nuanced than the first, and at the same time, it is the only one that gives access to the higher dimensions of spirit."

"Yes, but even if they are ignorant, people often live a life that seems good and even happy or abundant," I said. "Well, at least what they consider to be happiness and fulfillment."

"That is true," responded the lama. "They live but in ignorance, and this is exactly why they suffer. Suffering and ignorance complete and fuel one another. However, there is a hidden meaning even in this as only when suffering and troubles reach an unbearable threshold, which sometimes happens after tens or hundreds of successive lives, does a man realize that he can no longer continue that way. That is an essential moment in his evolution starting from which he begins to be more and more aware of his integration within the universe. Of course, there might still be numerous falls and comebacks of his on this path, but it is important that he already has planted in his consciousness and his inner perception the necessity to change something fundamental within himself, and this thought will always act as an impulse to propel him higher and higher."

Listening to what Repa Sundhi was saying, I was musing that ignorance is like night time for a man's understanding, like a thick fog that darkens his thinking.

"As far as I can tell, the condition of the ignorant one is not too far from that of an unknowing animal," I voiced my inner reflections.

"Even if it might seem exaggerated, know that it reflects the reality," the lama said. "In principle, it all starts from the fundamental difference between man and animal which is self-consciousness. The issue is simple. While a man knows he exists, meaning that he is self aware and can act in a determined way, the animal acts only by instinct, without knowing it exists. The life of an animal is reduced to a few spontaneous inner impulses and a very limited range of emotions. Nevertheless, among animals, as well as among people, there are noticeable differences that endow some of them, when reaching a certain evolutionary stage, with a rudimentary consciousness that further aids their leap towards the status of a human being with self awareness. It is obvious, for example, that between a mole and a dolphin there are great differences in regards to the possibilities of understanding and having communication with a being having superior conscious structures, like a man."

"You mean that the same evolutionary process from a form of inferior consciousness to one of superior consciousness remains valid anywhere else in the physical universe?" I intervened.

"Of course. Besides, you already know how diverse life is within our galaxy. In comparison with our galaxy, however, which is almost nothing, you would be much more surprised to discover an almost unimaginable grandeur in the diversity of life throughout the rest of the universe. A form will always adapt to the specific life conditions existent in the respective corner of the universe whether or not these correspond to the conditions of a human's life. Hence, intelligent forms in the universe are very different and only an immense ego and never ending stupidity can make people think they are alone in a truly gigantic universe whose real dimensions cannot be conceived or logically understood by the mind's assessment system.

"On the other hand, this physical universe is much smaller than the astral and mental universes which in turn are much smaller than the causal universe. Each of these has a practically infinite number of developmental possibilities regarding form and energy that is materialized into a specific type of matter and substance. For example, astral 'matter' is much more subtle than so called touchable physical matter which humans are used to. In turn, 'the substance' specific to the mental plane is more subtle than the astral 'substance' of emotions and the causal 'matter' is much more refined than the mental one.

"We are thus talking about a minimal intuition that man needs and a common sense issue for him to be able to realize that this colossal unfolding of forces and energies within the Creation is not just for his sake even if he thinks himself to be the only inhabitant of the infinite space surrounding him. What is common to all planes of existence, be it physical or subtle, is that they are structured with strict hierarchies depending upon one's degree of evolution and spiritual development. And, as the degree of evolution throughout the chain of transformations is directly proportional to the degree of knowledge, we reach the same problem we started with: namely, that the one who knows has power and this power gives him access to higher and higher dimensions of creation. Of course, I believe you already inferred that the power I'm referring to is not physical strength, financial power, or political power. All these are partial and very limited forms of the power the wise one achieves."

"So, everything is practically reduced to the evolution of consciousness," I concluded. "During this process, ignorance is gradually overcome by knowledge and this is how you explain why some people can do more and better than others."

"The degree of development of one's consciousness attracts the development of the form, or in other worlds, of the material 'carcass' that allows the further evolution of that individual consciousness," Repa Sundhi explained. "The mineral, vegetable, animal worlds and finally the human one derive from one another in this order. But, it would take too long and involve numerous explanations to right now get into details of the way this passing is realized and its specific conditions as well as the particularities of every world. That's why I will limit myself to explaining just some aspects about man and animals as in their case the consciousness begins to take on more evolved forms. I was telling you that although there is a fundamental difference between the two worlds, men often behave like animals and can even reach a lower stage than that."

Being of the same opinion myself, I could not help but notice that the astounding fall of Humankind is probably due to an acute form of ignorance.

"Nonetheless, how is it that man, who already possesses the spark of self-consciousness and knows he is an individual amongst others, manages to fall to a much inferior level?" I asked. "What kind of ignorance is that?"

Repa Sundhi seemed pleased that we had reached this point in our discussion.

"This truly is a more special issue," he answered. "It is so because with the feeling of individuality that gives him a purpose in life, man at the same time also has by default the individual free will to act and his actions can, of course, be good or bad. Unlike him, an animal does not act out of free will. If there are moments when it seems like it does, these are just incipient aspects of individual will. All actions made by an animal are determined by instinct and habit, including his attitudes of attachment or devotion. Of course, with the passing of time, these ensure the animal's evolution towards the status of human being, but it must be pointed out that it doesn't have a will of its own because it doesn't have a consciousness of its own and doesn't know it exists as an individual. An animal can recognize many beings and objects around him and can even make certain simple connections or manifest emotions, but all these nonetheless come only out of instinct and habit. That is why we can't talk of an individual consciousness within members of the animal kingdom. Unlike man, animals have a group consciousness out of which periodically, and as a result of a cumuli of experience, one of the members of that species makes a leap to a superior evolutionary level. This superior level can even mean a more evolved species of animals or the status of a human being. In such cases, that member of the animal species is a 'fragment' of the group consciousness; or better said, a quintessence of the evolutionary and experience level of that species at that precise time. Therefore, he is promoted in a superior stage of becoming. Gradually, it acquires the clearer and clearer awareness of its individuality until it reaches the stage of human being.

"Here, although the leap of consciousness to human status is huge compared to the previous existential conditions, the responsibility for the actions and doings committed belong solely to the individual. As I told you, the animal acts out of instinct and even if his actions are sometimes ferocious, they are either done in self-defense or in order to feed. These are not considered individual actions as an animal doesn't have the awareness of the nature of his acts; its actions being integrated at the level of the group consciousness of the species it belongs to. In such a manner does the consciousness of the respective species gain experience.

"In the case of the human, it is completely different as all that he acts, speaks and thinks is according to his own will, assuming that he is physically, mentally and psychically healthy. This free will is what gives him the possibility to consciously choose one option or the other and can determine whether he will go either on the path of evolution and good or on the one of perdition and suffering.

"Being human does not spare him the oppression of ignorance. If he chooses to do bad deeds, be violent, tough, stony, despotic or even kill, all these will 'count' in his own destiny or karma and he will have to pay like for like in future lives. All the vices of humanity, starting with pettiness, hypocrisy, lies and progressing to destructive vanity, acerbic greed, chaining attachment, and poisonous jealousy are actions that darken a man's soul like cinder and black smoke.

"Unlike him, an animal will act strictly by virtue of preservation, feeding and reproductive instinct. It is not capable of the unbelievable misery that some people are capable of inflicting nor their abominable actions or distasteful subterfuges used to serve their selfish purposes. This is why I was telling you that, unfortunately, man will sometimes fall lower than an animal because even though he is capable of noticing, judging and understanding the evil nature of these actions, he still commits them. This is actually the essence of sin and mistake. Man will always end up where the thread of past actions takes him, no matter if he is aware of it or not."

"How is it possible for humanity to be in such ruin though?" I asked, slightly confused. "Is ignorance so dramatic?"

"If you correctly understand the way these aspects are connected in the universe, all will be very clear. Ignorance determines erroneous actions and these, in turn, determine a cumulus of negative karma; namely, a hard destiny. In turn, this enchains the respective human being with limitations imposed by the mistakes he's committed and the process continues like an apparent vicious circle.

"Coming out of such a lamentable condition can only be done gradually and with a constant and intense effort from the part of the respective being in an effort to transform and orient the nature of his actions towards virtuosity. He can sometimes feel so desperate and hopeless when facing life's problems and hardships that he can be tempted to take his own life thinking that maybe this way he'll escape from it all. This is a huge mistake and constitutes a severe blockage on the evolutionary path."

I then remembered Elinor's remarks pertaining to this subject. Repa Sundhi completed what I already knew.

"Those who resort to such a reckless act are usually psychically and mentally unstable people or those who manifest demonic influences in their personality. These aspects may not be noticed by the people around the suicidal person and can even seem unreasonable compared to his life up to that time. People's stupidity and ignorance, however, cannot be substituted for truth."

I was amazed that the lama seemed to know very well what I had talked about with Elinor before his arrival. Nonetheless, I noticed that he was discretely pointing only to those aspects of the conversation he considered important and that he wanted me to deepen my understanding of. His power of telepathic knowledge was formidable.

"Generally speaking, man lives an almost continuous drama of manifestations," he continued to speak.

"Without even suspecting the fact that there is a profound meaning of life in the universe and that there are certain fundamental and immutable laws that act in a perfect balance, the ignorant usually take the bad as good and the other way around. Left to his own devices, they are like a leaf carried by the wind or like a carriage without a driver to rein the scared horses. Often acting blindly, without thinking at all and under the impulse of his destiny, the ignorant man attracts many energies in his aura that will make him live his life in a larvae-like inferior state.

"Between this deplorable state and the one in which the human being is superior, there is a colossal difference which, paradoxically, is very rarely recognized by ordinary men. This is explained by the fact that the one who lives in a limited area of perception and knowledge does not have the capacity to easily understand what is superior to him as he has no comparison. Furthermore, he notices that many of his life principles are malefic and opposed to the universal harmony; and, together with his petty prejudices, are the complete opposite of the behavior and vision over life of a wise person. Confused, the ignorant then feels that, in order to transform, he needs to completely change his entire life vision which undoubtedly involves great effort, at least in the beginning. Often, he is not willing to undertake this effort. Moreover, he comes to consider that the principles and the profoundly spiritual way of life of the wise one are, in fact, mistaken and need to be stigmatised by society. The ignorant one, who then becomes malevolent, is supported in his intercession by the acceptance and opinion of the majority who are also blind. In fact, this kind of action expresses, in a subtle plane of existence, the raging fear of people. This applies in particular to the rich ones or those of the ruling elite who are afraid of losing their privileges, their influence and political power, and even their wealth. This way of action was and is aimed especially at great spiritual reformers of Humankind and at those who share with others their innovative ideas about the freedom of the spirit, purity of life, honor and divine love. Being considered social threats, they are rapidly oppressed and the public opinion is directed and manipulated by means of false information so that it becomes a common front against the accused.

"As you already know, truth always wins; but this doesn't mean there's no suffering. Suffering appears every time there is a breach of the cosmic laws of harmony and balance, be it by actions done in the present time or by the agency of destiny reflecting the bad acts of the past and previous lives. You must know, however, that even suffering has a special meaning within the Creation. Its main 'purpose' is not to punish but to correct man's wrong attitudes regarding the life he is living. As much as he can see his mistake and learn from it, without repeating it later, the suffering disappears. If the man persists in his error and does not understand the hidden causes of his suffering, this will then amplify more and more and make his life a real nightmare."

I was touched and felt cold shivers along my spine. Repa Sundhi's explanation had stirred within me the exaltation of desire of not doing wrong but also the worry for the bad deeds I had done in other lives. I confessed my thoughts to him, but he laughed kindly, reassuring me.

"Lamentations for mistakes made in previous lives or the present one are pointless unless they allow you to lucidly observe their maleficent nature. To be honest, the term sufferance is only relative as the man receives only what he gave a long time ago."

"I also spoke with Elinor about this aspect," I said. "I was wondering though if things are really that rigorous."

Repa Sundhi was very firm in his answer.

"The law of karma acts inexorably and it is extremely precise. Nevertheless, divine grace often acts in a way so as to make man's many troubles and suffering throughout his life easier to cope with; especially when he sincerely regrets in his heart the mistakes he's done and understands that is not the way he needs to act. If it were not for this divine support, which is often called Providence, it is probable that the human being would be wiped out by the burden of sufferance he needs to endure as a result of his bad deeds. But, as you also know, God does not want the destruction of the sinner, but his rehabilitation.

"This is exactly why I am telling you that the only way to return to and manifest a divinely integrated existence is by way of spiritual knowledge, supreme amongst the other kinds of knowledge. When a being knows on this level, he has at his disposal a way to tune in with all that is superior in the universe. Then, knowing its fundamental structures and laws, he can choose. Namely, he can use his free will in a positive direction. Unfortunately, as you very well know, there are many beings that choose the negative path and that is truly sad for their future karma. The one who is beneficially oriented can engage his own will more and more in order to attract elevated vibrations in his aura which will give him essential support in all the actions he carries on."

Repa Sundhi stopped his explanations to ask me if I was tired. I told him that I rarely felt as good as I did then and thanked him for his care and attention. Although I aimed to deepen my spiritual knowledge during the last year, after Cezar left for the Great Expedition, I often felt the absence of a competent guide to explain the subtleties of some difficult aspects that I could not understand. My sporadic meditations did not always manage to pinpoint the hidden characteristics of some esoteric notions or concepts. This sometimes made me feel alone and helpless. Cezar had been so busy that I was only able to meet with him twice. That was when he shared some of the astounding mysteries of that event. So, I was extremely happy to find out as much information as possible regarding some subjects I had not managed to study thoroughly until that night.

On the other hand, I was intrigued by the real purpose of this meeting. What was the actual reason why Repa Sundhi wanted to speak to me?

"Yes, I think the time has also come to discuss this aspect," he answered. "It is already very late and there are still many things to do before we go."

"I do not know anything about any departure," I said cautiously, raising my eyebrows in surprise.

"It is very important that you trust us and what I am telling you now," he responded. "It is not necessary to ask too many questions now. You will later be helped to understand everything from a perspective you are still far from even inferring.

"We will have to make a short journey, and we will leave three days from now. Elinor will take care of everything that is needed. In the meantime, I will have some things to sort out so I am not going to see you until then. I insistently ask though that during these days you do not talk to anyone about what you are going to do or the fact that you met me. Besides, it is very unlikely anyone would believe you."

I felt completely taken by surprise. I did not know where I was going, what I needed to take with me, or what would be the duration of our travel; but especially, I did not know the reason why I was invited on this trip.

"There are plenty of unknown points," I said. "Of course, it is not an issue for me to arrange my business in the time we have left, but at least tell me how long we will be gone for."

"One day," the Tibetan answered tersely. "Well, at least in the human system of temporal evaluation. Don't worry. You don't need to pack anything. Think that you are going for a walk in the park although I can assure you that the stakes are much higher," he added in a joking manner.

"I don't understand why you are not telling me where we're going," I insisted. "I think it's only natural to tell me at least that, don't you think? I like mystery. I am attracted by unknown situations, but in this case, I think I should know some elements as well."

"There are mysteries and mysteries," the lama answered. "Some aspects must be revealed at the right time. Otherwise, there is a possibility that the entire action could be endangered. This can be due to a lack of self control with regard to emotions and thought that can cause one to act chaotically. Although you know many initiatory aspects and have been faced with very shocking realities for a normal human, I feel that you are still not ready to know beforehand what is going to happen in a couple of days. This is exactly why I asked you to trust us completely. Your experience will be very intense. It is one thing to read in books or hear something but completely something else to be personally faced with that reality. Be at peace. We will also be with you. There's nothing to be afraid of."

Peace and calm were the last things on my mind after hearing Repa Sundhi's pep talk.

"I think that uncertainty will generate more thoughts than knowing what to expect," I said timidly.

"I could, of course, reveal to you the reason for this travel; but this case is very special and must be treated very carefully. There are several reasons why it is better to proceed this way. First of all, I suggested this way of action as the most appropriate one as there are also perturbing forces that will find out the purpose of our departure and will want to hinder it by any means. I need to sort these things out and protect the mission. Besides, this is why I am accompanied by the yidam who is an important stabilizing agent in such dangerous circumstances."

"But, you said that the yidam is not your creation! How did he then end up in your company?" I asked.

"If I would give you a detailed answer to this question, I would have to reveal the reason of the trip we are taking. So, I will only give you a general view in order to appease your mental agitation a little bit. We will go to a certain area in the Apuseni Mountains where you will meet someone. This event, however, will happen under very special circumstances. You will see and understand everything at the right time. This yidam has great experience in regards to the terrestrial plane and was asked to accompany me in this mission. Know that it is not the first time he has helped me in what I have to do on Earth," Repa Sundhi added, looking up at the yidam who remained motionless, staring with his eyes wide open at an imaginary point somewhere far away.

"If you are taking such precautionary measures, it means that there could be some real problems," I reflected out loud.

"Yes, I already told you that," he replied. "The meeting you will have is truly special and involves some space-time modifications that can become breaches for some adverse forces. If there is no solid protection, these can perturb the phenomena and hinder its development. I am telling you again, however, that you shouldn't be afraid as you'll be protected."

I was wondering how much Repa Sundhi's words were managing to calm me. My body was shaking imperceptibly as a result of a profound emotion but also from impatience to find out what was actually going on behind this mystery. Who was I going to meet? Why were all of these intermediary stages necessary? What strange phenomena was going to happen and who was going to create it? Instead of all these, I asked Repa Sundhi a completely different question.

"I am honestly telling you that I don't understand why I in particular have to face all these challenges! I am only at the beginning of a spiritual path and my knowledge still has so many missing pieces. It's true that I was a witness to some extraordinary events; but from what you are telling me and I infer is coming in the future, I'm not sure I'm the right person."

The lama answered in a very serious voice.

"You observation is egotistic and proves a hidden vanity of which you probably are not even aware right now. Why is it of interest that you don't know too much of what is going to happen? If I were to tell you right now, 'You are right. Maybe I didn't correctly assess the situation and I now realize that in fact you can't cope with it as you are not ready yet!' Do you think you'll be joyful? Do you think you will instantly accept it and go home, happy that you were relieved of a burden? I can assure you that this wouldn't be your inner reaction. You would end up feeling frustrated and regret that you even considered this proposition. You see, that's why it is very good to always say what you actually feel in the depths of your heart as only that has meaning, only that truly has power and impact over others. Leave the verbal and behavioral artifices to the ones who don't know all these things. In time, they will too awaken to a more profound reality and will then teach others how to act correctly.

"Rest assured that if you were called to realize this action, it is not at all by chance. There are, of course, some hidden reasons related to your being that you obviously don't know now; but they justify all that's been geared up to facilitate the present situation. So, be sincerely humble and not just for show as this way you will become pure and untouchable to negative influences."

After this "cold shower" that I honestly did not expect, I have decided to pay more attention to what I feel, think and speak. Carefully analyzing myself, I noticed that the lama was perfectly right. Although I had been sincere with my words, I however had more profound intentions that did not totally correspond to what I said.

I realize that the true battle to reach perfection happens inside at the core and in the depths of the mind and soul. Even the apparently insignificant malignant aspects and tendencies, that for some are part of their normal daily attitude, must be identified and eliminated. No stain is admitted if you truly want to be perfect.

"Nonetheless, these are simple situations that – if there's interest and willingness – can be solved very quickly," the lama continued to explain. "The true problems appear when a man gets into major negative habits. Unpleasant experiences in life fuel negative and inferior feelings in many people with emotions like hate, malice, anger or revenge. For the ignorant one, the persistence of such states automatically attracts them towards the inferior worlds or planes of the universe. These negative feelings and emotions are like seeds that a man sows in his soul which, of course, will bear fruits to match. You know very well that if you sow wind you reap whirlwind. Or, so that you understand better, you can't sow a field with weed seeds and expect a plentiful wheat harvest. It's impossible for people to sow hate, quarrel, malice and then reap something good and harmonious. Let's say you just washed your shirt which is now immaculately white and then went for a walk in town. You notice, however, that there is an ink stain remaining that is in contrast with the impeccable white of the material. Can you say that you are satisfied and have reached perfection in cleaning that shirt? Do you think that others won't notice the black stain? On the contrary, it will stand out more on the immaculate white background of the shirt and unpleasantly affect them.

"The more a person evolves and comes closer to perfection, the more careful and responsible he must be, even of the most insignificant actions. At that point, any inappropriate remark, inadequate act or negative feature of his character will be immediately noticed by those around him because they will stand out from the good and relatively balanced background of that person. If that remark, deed, feature or character trait would have been of a normal human, no one would pay much attention as it would have been part of a common and at the same time inferior characteristic of that man. It wouldn't have stood out at all. In the case of a wise man or a saint, however, a mistake – no matter how small – will soon reach monstrous proportions in the eyes of ordinary people. That is why I was telling you that spiritual evolution brings with it the need to be responsible in order to eliminate all the stains of gross inferior feelings and manifestations that are common to most people. Perfection is hard to reach; but once reached, the realization is total and the reward never-ending."

Repa Sundhi stopped and looked at his watch.

"It is very late," he said. "I think it's time to part as there are still some things to sort out before departure."

Elinor then suggested I stay overnight at his villa, but after a quick thought, I declined politely. I wanted to analyze in peace and quiet all of the aspects of this memorable day that had marked me so deeply. In addition to that, I felt the need to walk to my house. I had two days to reflect on what had happened and to arrange for my absence. It was established that on the third day, very early in the morning, we were going towards the goal of our journey of which I had only a vague idea.

Out of the few clues I got from Repa Sundhi, I had understood two essential aspects: that unusual phenomena were going to occur that could be accompanied by manifestations against us; and that no matter what I believed of this action and its impact on me, the best solution was to totally accept it.

I really hoped to be worthy of Repa Sundhi's expectation. Between you and me, what I lived during that expedition shook me so profoundly that there have been moments when my senses just stopped working and I did not know if I was still alive or dead. I was, however, helped to safely overcome the intense emotions I felt then and thus obtain a much ampler vision over the manifested reality, both physical and subtle.

I got out of the armchair to say goodbye to Repa Sundhi and bowed in front of the yidam who looked at me kindly. But while Elinor was showing us out in the hallway, I noticed how the yidam's giant body became more and more transparent until it disappeared completely in just a few seconds. The lama then explained that the yidam had to complete a certain task that requires his presence somewhere else. After we set a few more details of the meeting that was to happen in three days time, we all said goodbye; but I stayed a little longer with Elinor who had asked me to wait for him. He soon came back and gave me a pocket watch that looked well-worn.

"It belonged to my ancestor and is almost three hundred years old. The inset is an etching of his face. It's exactly as he looked when I met him in Brussels."

I looked at the engraved image of a very distinguished young man with long hair and a bow tie. The very old and worn watch was a testament of long gone times and touching it made me feel the subtle shiver of mystery surrounding the person in the engraving. My entire being was then overwhelmed by the nostalgia of the long gone times and places which that man had witnessed.

I thanked Elinor for his gesture and said goodbye. I then went out to the long deserted street at the same time as raindrops began to fall. Although I was expecting to still see Repa Sundhi's silhouette, I noticed he had vanished. Refusing to analyze this new enigma, I strolled on my way towards the magical future that awaited me.

3

MACHANDI

Contrary to my expectations, I was quite calm and focused on preparing for my departure during the following two days. Although I intensely remembered many of the puzzling elements of my meeting with Elinor and Repa Sundhi, I was not at all agitated but simply trying to analyze in depth what had been revealed to me.

Just as it had been established, I phoned Elinor the evening before we left to find out if the plans for our journey were still valid. After receiving his confirmation, I spent the few remaining hours prior to our meeting trying to sleep. I soon discovered this to be quite a difficult task. As soon as I closed my eyes, my mind was invaded by the image of an aesthetic mountain landscape where the cliffs and valleys were covered in ice and snow. Two peaks towered over the horizon, basking in the red-orange sunset. The overview was desolate and a cold wind blew strongly, ruffling the few lichens growing in a dried up riverbank.

I tossed and turned in my bed without understanding the significance or message of that vision. Every time I closed my eyes and tried to fall asleep, it came back to me very clearly and with an amazing realism. Plus, when I was seeing the landscape, I perceived it with all of my senses so that I actually became very cold and used several blankets to cover myself. Eventually, after remaining on the border between wakefulness and sleep for a long time, I fell asleep but without dreaming. My absorption into the sleep state was so deep that when the alarm went off it took me a few good seconds to realize what was actually happening. The sound of the alarm was reaching me as if from very far away, gradually getting closer and closer. I finally awoke and noticed with amazement and great joy that I also felt excellent and very well rested. In high spirits, I took a cab to Elinor's villa; but as a precautionary measure, I gave the driver an address a few streets away.

When I arrived, Elinor and Repa Sundhi were already there waiting for me. I thought I was late, but they reassured me and told me everything was ready for our journey.

"Isn't the yidam accompanying us?" I asked in surprise, noticing that the deity was not in the house.

"Yes, but he will join us at some point on our way," the lama answered without any other details.

We got into Elinor's car, a very luxurious jeep that was parked in front of the house. In order to be able to talk easily during the journey, the lama proposed I stay with him in the back seats and I gladly accepted.

It was almost five in the morning when we left. The clear starry sky was forecasting a beautiful day. Besides that, the beginning of this particular November was proving to be very warm with only rare and short rains. I observed that if we needed to do any mountaineering that we would probably have very good weather for it. In response, Repa Sundhi explained that our efforts were not going to be great and that the weather would not be of much importance. His answer confused me a bit, but I did not ask for clarifications.

As Elinor drove fast, it took us only two hours to reach the foothills of the Southern Carpathians that we had to cross. I was enchanted as I admired the wonderful landscape that basked in the superb light of the sunrise. I noticed that to our right, not far away from the area we were passing through, was the secret location in the Bucegi Mountains that I had visited more than a year before.

"That very special place will play an important role in the near future of Romania," the lama said unexpectedly. "The discovery was not at all by chance and the expedition led by Cezar was a first sign of the coming changes, not only regarding Romania but the entire planet. The causes that will lead to these transformations are so complex that they can't be comprehended or understood by a normal human mind. That is why the few who are acting to pave the way, so to speak, are often supported by angelic entities belonging to different hierarchical categories of manifestation. In the oriental tradition, these are called deities. It is good to know that they are organized in a pyramidal hierarchy that pretty much follows the same principles and structure as a company or industrial enterprise in modern society."

"Cezar spoke only vaguely about the help some angelic entities unconditionally offer to humanity," I said. "I never understood though how this help is manifested or how it can be perceived here in the physical plane."

"Subtle purification is an important aspect of what these beings belonging to superior astral worlds are doing at the level of one country or even at the level of the entire planet," the lama said. "I hope that you are at least partly familiarized with this. In essence, it refers to some subtle realities that modern science rejects or at least ignores.

"Just as the human being has a bioenergetic aura so does the Earth. Due to the subtle bioenergetic field emanated by its biosphere, it has an 'aura' of its own. Of course, unlike the aura of a human, the aura of the planet is gigantic. The characteristics of the two auras, however, are just the same as the energetic processes happening within them are identical in principle. For example, a man's aura can gradually become impure due to his unhealthy diet and the impure and gross environment he lives in, but it is at its most acute and profound following the actions a man does, especially mental acts or thoughts. In regards to the Earth's aura, its condition depends on the nature of the physical, mental and verbal actions of the beings living on the planet's surface."

For me, it was starting to be easy to conceive and assimilate this information, but I was not too sure it could be "stomached" by regular people.

"Unfortunately, these things are exactly as you said for such people," Repa Sundhi admitted. "A man that is not aware of or even informed of his own subtle aura cannot believe that the planet he's living on is itself a 'being' with a gigantic aura. For an experienced clairvoyant, however, this is only too obvious. They have free and unlimited access to the astral plane and can, in certain circumstances, perceive the actual aura of the planet which is very 'charged.'"

"I know that the aura of a being can give much information about their physical and psychic state, but is this also valid in regards to the destiny of that respective being?" I asked. "I mean, does our aura contain information about our karma?"

"The energetic structure of the aura is very complex," he responded, "but an essential part of it is that within it is encoded practically any information about that man that is more or less hidden in specific ways. Hence, the correct 'reading' of the aura can foresee the nature of a future disease, its seriousness, or even the death of that respective being if certain particular signs are seen. Usually, these 'symptoms' are the result of some karmic mistakes made in previous lives that were transmitted into the present life and have even been unconsciously accentuated by that person. Such karmic influences of a subtle energetic nature appear in the aura as dark vortexes and are almost black in very serious cases. From the exterior to the interior, they look like a deep 'funnel' towards the body outline. In a way, they can be likened in form and structure with a boil. Their presence in the aura is most often a sign of destiny for that person's life.

"It's very similar for the Earth's aura. The most harmful elements that contributed to it becoming impure are men's vices and misdeeds to which you can add wrongly orientated technology. The situation is becoming acute because of the great number of human beings living on the surface of the planet who act wrongly and tip the balance to the negative side."

After a short break, during which I intensely analyzed the

information I had just heard, the lama felt the need to give me further explanations.

"The aura is, in fact, a subtle energetic cumulus and depends upon the predominant nature of the energies that comprise it. Things here are relatively simple: if you act only beneficially then you accumulate positive energies of a beneficial nature in your aura. Such an aura is bright, alive, active and radiant. But for those who fall prey to vices and persevere in perverse and negative thinking, their aura is gradually becoming more and more impure with maleficent energies. These make it dull, tarnished, and dominated by dark colors like muddy green, brown, dark red and even areas of dark grey and black.

"These particularities of the aura are intimately correlated with destiny's traits. The interaction between human beings or between them and the things or phenomena surrounding them is firstly an energetic interaction at the subtle level of the aura. This is by virtue of the known principle that 'birds of a feather flock together,' and this principle is valid everywhere throughout the Creation. That is why a human being that is evil and even satanic in his behavior will never be capable of doing good deeds. For the same reason, you will almost never see a gang of villains going to church and enjoying the company of priests and saints in order to repent and transform their lives. Those unfortunate beings will continue to act by virtue of the predominantly negative energetic vibrations that they have in their aura and will associate with people of the same nature, outdoing one another in new misdoings. As I have already told you, they thus sow the seeds of a bitter destiny that they will have to live with the same intensity of loss and suffering that they caused others."

"I've met people who mockingly say that they will have enough time afterwards to 'pay' for the mistakes done at the present," I said. "Personally, I think this is a very detrimental vision of reality."

"It is true that in their unawareness and ignorance, many people let themselves be tempted by their mind's voice and not their heart's," responded the lama. "For example, some are tempted to take advantage of life's 'pleasures' as much as possible; and in a selfish way, not make allowance for the bad seeds they then sow. These people think they are going to have enough time later in life to 'consume' these negative effects or, in other words, pay them off. I have to tell you though that this is the sign of great stupidity. It is similar to saying that you want to enter the despicable mud found in a pond just so you can then get out and wash it off. Of course, this is possible but it will involve more effort and you will need more time to clean the 'mud' you're covered in. What then is the use of such action? The merits you accumulated with difficulty at some point in your life will be quickly annihilated by bad actions that bring a so-called satisfaction that is only partial and ephemeral."

I was starting to realize that such a sombre perspective was similar to the toil of Sisyphus, and the only explanation I could find in such cases was the weakness of people when facing the ephemeral temptations of the material world. I understood that negative emotions generate quite rapidly in the human being as inferior and gross preoccupations which include the avid tendency to gain, opulent luxury, fame and the fight for power. All of these have a tendency to generate feelings of greed, insensitivity, meanness, envy, selfishness, fury or revenge. I then asked Repa Sundhi to what extent all of these negative emotions affect the human aura.

"These emotions are, in fact, subtle energies with a gross frequency of vibration. If they are not quickly removed or given up fast in order to be replaced with their exact opposite, they will set in at the level of the aura and various corresponding body organs which will cause psychic disturbances, serious diseases and illnesses. In a similar way, this process happens in the Earth's aura which is deeply influenced by the aura of the human beings that live on it.

"Unfortunately, the present situation of the planet's aura is quite critical. As it stands now, it can be likened to the aura of a gravely sick person. In such a situation, it is natural to follow a purification 'treatment' in order to cure the disease. Just as in a human being, the planet will be 'convulsing' or undergo other similar phenomena that people living on its surface will perceive as apocalyptic events. There's nothing supernatural about this. It is just a counter-balancing effect of the negative 'charge.' In other words, the planet's negative karma has reached a critical point and is thus influencing the destiny of Humankind."

"I have also spoken with Elinor about some aspects that are related to destiny, and I think I understand its formative mechanism," I then told Repa Sundhi.

"Yes," he said. "In principle, the process is quite simple. Every human being is characterized by a specific energy that determines a certain general mental and soul state. This general state will then create channels through which some dominant mental tendencies will manifest in correlation with the feelings and energy of that human. Then, the dominating tendencies will generate an entire series of other habits and tendencies that structure most of that person's future destiny.

"This is how you explain why some people with a gross energy manifest gross feelings and ideas. They are not satisfied with their opinions and start judging others after their own meanness, scepticism and perversity. All these happen because they cannot conceive that others could be different from themselves. In such circumstances, the evolutionary path of such beings will be long and difficult as they have not yet awakened the beneficial force of their subtle structure, and this is exactly why they do not have what it takes to support a balanced and harmonious life.

"You can thus understand why certain spiritual leaps do not happen overnight. In the case of beings who are only starting to awaken spiritually, the energetic cumuli one has is not great enough. That is to say, it is not predominant. In such circumstances, the feelings and states that being is faced with will be mixed, meaning some will be good but most of it will be bad.

Due to several factors, both internal and external, this will generate a continuous fluctuation of the being between opposite poles. For example, if maleficent accumulations are present in the nature of that being when he comes into contact with a maleficent ambiance, he will be affected and will relive states that he abhors. A being who has accumulated beneficial energy par excellence will not have any maleficent reaction if in the same negative ambiance. The one who has even a little maleficent cumulus in his aura will feel, in a reduced way, that environment. In other words, he will still notice that the respective ambiance is bad. By the opposite, a totally beneficial being, even when coming into contact with that inferior environment, will not perceive it as such. He will, of course, be aware of its nature due to the reactions of those who are found there. Nevertheless, he will remain completely unaffected because there are no connections in his aura to those negative energetic manifestations. This is a very important aspect and this is why I want you to understand it well," Repa Sundhi added in an emphatic voice.

After thinking for a little while, I said, "I very well realize that it is essential to accumulate as many beneficial and elevated energies as possible in my aura in order to generate a state of balance and harmony in my structure."

"More than that, the accumulations that a being gets in his aura will be the ones triggering all the leaps to come in that being's spiritual evolution," Repa Sundhi completed. "You must know that by continuing to accumulate, the chance of evolutionary leaps can always appear. It's good that you understand the necessity to accumulate exclusively positive energies at the level of the aura. Afterwards, as I told you before, these accumulations will add up and generate the premise for an evolutionary leap towards an accelerated evolution.

"The same is valid for spiritual regress or involution. But we are not talking anymore about a leap in this case. A leap is a synonym with going forwards, but a fall represents a downfall of the being into the abyss of evil. For as long as there's still evil in man, he will be vulnerable as what is already in the being will always attract something similar."

"But how will we then ever manage to accumulate merits and beneficial energies?" I asked, confused.

"There are enough possibilities to use one's individual will so as to annihilate the negative accumulations. For example, one way is to act the opposite to the maleficent tendency that is then felt within. If he is about to be overcome by a state of anger and fury then he will have to control himself and patiently induce a state of calm and love for the other being upon whom he wanted to project the malefic energies. All of these involve effort, but you must know that you can't succeed without effort."

"I feel confident and willing to make this effort!" I said, suddenly overcome by a very good mood.

"Excellent! This means that you are optimistic and belong to those who already have a beneficial predominance in their aura. The pessimists are the ones with malefic, negative, and destructive predominance in the structure of their aura."

Glad that I understood these fundamental aspects of existence and evolution in manifestation, I then expressed my gratitude towards Repa Sundhi for the patience and kindness he demonstrated when explaining these essential truths to me that now seemed very simple.

"It is true that these things now look simple and obvious, but do not forget that you can't reach it unless you 'nourish' yourself with essences."

"I've assented," I said, shaking my head.

I was impressed by the special force of the lama's words and his profound knowledge. What he said brightened my understanding and seemed to forever pierce my consciousness. I then asked him about the ways the deities of the subtle planes of Creation help humanity and the entire planet to cross this critical stage of their existence.

"Even in this case, it is still a matter of humanity's choice," answered Repa Sundhi. The angelic entities, deities and all those helping the "spiritualization" of the planet act due to their own beliefs and altruistic impulses, but their help could be much more substantial if men would invoke it and ask for it in a sentient way. This would be a big step forward as it would mean that they are awakening out of their 'numbness' and realizing the decadence that humanity is in. Their prayers and good thoughts would immensely contribute to the purification of the Earth's subtle aura. On the other hand, some subtle entities in the elevated planes of Creation impel certain human beings through teachings or revelations made in the dream state. These manifestations are so alive and powerful that they sometimes are ingrained in the consciousness of the one "living" it in the dream state even better then the events he's going through during the time he spends awake in the physical world."

I instantly remembered the image that had appeared obsessively in my mind before I fell asleep. I could not say it was a dream, but it was obvious that it was not physical reality either. I hesitated for a few moments preparing to tell Repa Sundhi about it, but I gave up when Elinor stopped in a parking place on the side of the road crossing the mountains. We stretched for a little while and admired the wonderful scenery surrounding us. I then ate something with Elinor who had brought all the necessary provisions. Repa Sundhi declined to eat and instead chose to walk higher up on the mountain's side, deep in his thoughts.

After approximately twenty minutes, we got back on the road and soon after we crossed the mountains leading into Transylvania. As we went off the main road and took a route towards the southern side of the Apuseni Mountains, it seemed like both Elinor and Repa Sundhi knew the way we were supposed to go. All this time, I had not asked for any details regarding our final destination nor did the lama mention any new elements. As we came closer to the smooth and very large mountainous plateaus specific to those mountains, I noticed that Repa Sundhi was becoming more and more quiet and focused. That is why I did not want to disturb him with any questions and just abandoned myself to the flow of events that were unfolding.

The jeep had left the secondary road for a while now and was climbing a country road that wound itself through several villages spread on the tall hillsides. At very close range, I could see the first summits that were covered in vast forests. Leaving behind us a last settlement of only a few houses, we entered a forest road that was surprisingly well maintained. You could tell that there had not been anyone going that way for a long time as the vegetation had grown wild in the road and by its sides. You could even see the wheel tracks which are normally encountered in such areas. The road sloped through the forest for approximately one and a half kilometers until it was blocked. All three of us got out of the car, and I saw a very large clearing through the trees that had been created by wood cutters. Only the stumps of the trees were left, partially covered by vegetation.

"We will walk from here," said Repa Sundhi. "There are no humans for miles around us, but you will be delighted by the scenery."

I then confessed that I did not have the necessary training to cross the mountains, my last attempt to do so being over ten years ago; but the lama assured me that I would not have to make too much of an effort as the route was easy and the slope was not that steep.

All three of us broke into the clearing. Only then did I realize that we were in fact right on the crest of the hill we had driven up earlier. I think that it was actually a part of the mountain range we had been looking at as it was much smaller than other crests and connected to the mountain through a not too deep and relatively narrow valley.

We crossed the clearing and walked towards the mountain through the tall and yielding grass which curiously enough was still green. The weather was warm and the mild breeze brought the smell of fallen leaves and damp earth. I then felt the first wafts of an unmistakable perfume I knew only too well. It was the smell of ambergris and myrrh that always accompanied the yidam. I commented to the others about it.

"I know. He's been with us for a little while," answered Repa Sundhi. "He has already announced a situation to me telepathically and you will soon be able to see his physical form."

Indeed, a few seconds later the yidam gradually materialized behind Repa Sundhi, next to his left shoulder. I noticed that this was not instantaneous materialization but rather a very fast process that went through two or three stages of compacting. First, the outline of his body manifested as a diffuse vapor in the atmosphere; then it intensified only in certain areas before making a complete appearance in its final phase. Even though I had already witnessed this process in a reverse fashion a couple of days ago in Elinor's house, my amazement was as great now as it was then, only now I refrained from expressing it.

The yidam's impressive stature gave me a feeling of profound safety and trust in the successful outcome of any problems. This feeling did not last long, however, as I gradually started to notice a paradoxical phenomenon that perturbed any logical analysis my brain could make which projected me into a state of total uncertainty.

The Translation

All the fantasy stories and scientific theories of parallel dimensions hold almost no value compared to directly experiencing this truth. In my case, my astonishment was even greater as I had the possibility of seeing in detail the actual interweaving of two planes of reality without it perturbing my senses in any way.

As we were walking through that valley, I noticed how the edges of the horizon, both on the left and the right, were becoming darker and darker, "narrowing" my field of vision. But at the same time, as if balancing it out, the frontline of the horizon seemed to deepen even more so as to "pull" the landscape with it. The dimming of the light on the sides made it look more like twilight, blurring the details in those areas. Up to that moment, however, those details had been very clear in the daylight. This very strange manifestation gave me the feeling that we were in a giant vat. The dimensions of the landscape, which until then had been logically interpreted by the brain, had become disproportionate and even tended to reverse their optic projection. What was far away was big and what we could see nearby was very small. I noticed immediately that this created an obvious state of confusion in my brain which generated a feeling of fear within my being. The shocking transformation I perceived in the surrounding environment, however, did not happen suddenly but gradually which allowed a certain "maneuvering space" to my capacity to understand.

It is very strange to walk through a certain area and have the feeling that the reality surrounding you is starting to reconfigure itself like in a cartoon. I noticed that the first impression that is then generated by the mind is one of hesitation and uncertainty. The brain very quickly analyzes all of the possible interpretations but still cannot find anything like it in one's previous experiences. It then tries to build, all by itself, a new model of what it perceives, but this extrapolation is unsuccessful as the basic laws of logic and physics of tridimensional space are not respected and these are the very basis of the interpretation. Thus, in a very short time, the brain "gives up" as it has already exhausted all the possibilities.

This new state of perception is, however, unfavorable to the usual mental condition as the mind has to always be busy, continuously needing something to analyze. That is why, in the unusual situation that I was in, it generated an acute feeling of inner fear by default which was really nothing else but my ego reacting with panic to the new reality I perceived. This was largely due to the ancestral survival instinct that exists in any being which, at the same time, chains us to the manifestation of our normal reality, forcing us, in a way, to "cling" to life, to experience, and to the exterior world.

At the same time as all of this was going on, I was aware that I was capable of lucidly observing the feeling of fear that had gripped me and was even able to rapidly analyze its causes and origin. This caused a shock in my entire being, forcing the clarity of a situation I had not even been aware of until then. I asked myself the following question: if, on the one hand, I am the one who lives the fear and anguish I was facing, then who was the one who was observing that emotion and contraction of my whole being? I was forced to admit that it was not someone else separate from me. I lived that fear myself and could say for certain that it was still me who was the one detachedly observing it. While the first feeling was giving me an acute state of contraction and discomfort within my entire being, the second one was calming me and lifting me, offering a state of great trust and safety. While I was profoundly absorbed in these reflections, Repa Sundhi addressed me without any introduction as if we were just resuming a prior discussion.

"Your inner observations are correct, but the confusion has not completely disappeared yet. You are very close to making a significant leap of consciousness and understanding of the complex relations between what is real and what is false. Now is a very good moment to realize that the phenomenal world is structured so as absorb all of man's attention in a wrong interpretative direction. It is a magical act, an excellent example of cosmic illusion. Apparently, no one nor no thing could convince a human being that the reality he lives in is not exactly as he perceives it. But, as you have the opportunity to see for yourself right now, this belief is erroneous. All of man's beliefs and prejudices regarding matter and the laws of classical physics are proven to be false and inapplicable. The problem is, that during his countless existences, the human being gradually fortified these false beliefs and prejudices in a central focus which he thinks represents his individuality."

"I don't understand very well," I said. "I think I am what, in fact, I am not?"

"Exactly. But it's not just you who does that but also any other being within the Creation. There are, of course, different grades of intensity. The greater the ignorance, the more a man is caught up in the toil of this illusion which he finds very difficult to get rid of. Analyze carefully the inner perception you just had. It's a good start. Can you tell which of the two 'identities' you were closer to before now?"

It was not too difficult to realize what he was saying so I answered immediately.

"Naturally, of the one who made me feel fear. It seems much stronger, much closer to me."

"'Me' who?" the lama asked. "Define 'me.'"

Suddenly I realized that I had no clear idea of who or what I truly am. My first tendency was to identify with the body, but even I, only at the beginning on the path of understanding certain initiatory aspects, knew that such an idea is, in fact, an aberration. How could I be, in my essence, this body when I cannot even be aware of it at all times? Not earlier than a few days, when I noticed that I was perfectly lucid, I had no perception of my body whatsoever and did not wish to either. The profound state of relaxation and dilation that had then been induced in me by the lama and the yidam caused me to transcend the perceptions of my body which are very limited. Even so, I continued to know that I exist but under no circumstances as a consistency of material physical form.

"Look for the answer," Repa Sundhi spurred me. "This is where the essence of existence lies. Whenever contradictory situations appear, carefully analyze the causes that led there. There can't be two truths in one. That is why you must correctly understand what the falsehood consists of. The main advantage of this is that you will never be tricked again into believing the falseness and it won't affect your existence as it did before then. If, for example, you profoundly understood that your real identity is not this body but a much more subtle reality, then you can be sure that you will not be confronted anymore with a whole series of false, pointless attitudes and perceptions. First, the fear of death will gradually disappear; then you will not pay excessive attention to the outer form of the body. Certain conceited attitudes will greatly fade and even disappear and you will become less selfish. But, you need to be careful as this is only a stage on the path of becoming, and you must not just stop at this point in the analysis. Its depths are unsuspected."

While Repa Sundhi was saying the last few words, I noticed that over the landscape we were passing through was appearing another one which, in the beginning, was like a film projection overlapping the physical reality we were in. Although the projected image was diffused, I could still tell it was a mountainous landscape but much rockier. I could see that the ground I was stepping on was the grass and vegetation of the Apuseni Mountains. At the same time, however, a translucent image of an arid mountain path was superimposed over it. Strewn with rocks, the path snaked between two slopes.

I stopped and almost rubbed my eyes to clear off the mirage. The other three stopped as well, looking at me. No one was saying anything and time seemed to have stopped, too. I looked around me. The lateral twilight seemed to have accentuated, climbing higher towards the zenith. In front of me, the gigantic summit of a rocky mountain was taking shape clearer and clearer over the much lower slopes of the forested Apuseni mountains towards which we were going. The intertwining of the two realities was creating an ambiguous state and even a feeling of uncertainty regarding the ground I was walking on.

The image of the sky was also changing as the time was passing. Its blue color and the bright sun I could see up to that time were more and more overtaken by a thick blanket of dark bluish clouds; but the latter did not quite manage to completely cover the image of the sun of my reality. The perspective I had was truly astounding and magnificent at the same time: the sun rays of my world were sometimes piercing through the threatening blanket of clouds of the reality overlapping it and was diffused in wonderful conical shapes on the mountain slopes. The grandeur of that unique spectacle can hardly be put into words. I was overwhelmed, but even so, I still had my self control. Instead of making desperate efforts to understand what was actually happening, I decided to observe, as calmly and as interestedly as I could, that amazing transformation of the landscape or, better said, of the reality I was in at that time.

The "replacement" of the old landscape with the new spatial projection of the arid rocky valley was almost complete. I could only see very few influences of the sun and areas of green vegetation here and there. These were more and more faded, however, and making room for the new spatial frame which was much harsher and wilder. In the beginning, it was just an unclear sensation; but as the transition ended, I was shocked with amazement. The mountainous area we were in now was exactly the one that obsessively appeared in my mind before we started on this journey!

"This is an important moment in your existence that will help you understand that phenomena are relative within manifestation. At the same time, you will believe that by profoundly meditating over its ephemeral nature, you will manage to obtain the almost magical control of the reality you live in. Then you will be able to determine yourself, at will, modifications or parallel translations of other worlds of the Creation, if that will be necessary at some point."

Repa Sundhi was talking slowly in a grave voice and looking into my eyes.

"I saw this place last night. It appeared in my mind as soon as I closed my eyes," I said, slightly disoriented. "I didn't know what it meant. And I still don't understand much even now."

"You were supported in this way so that the present won't shock you too much," the lama explained. "It is an area situated at great height, in one of Tibet's mountains."

I was left staring ahead.

"We are in Tibet now?" I stammered.

"Yes, the translation is complete. But don't worry. The whole process is reversible," the lama assured me.

"But I still don't understand. Why all of this? Why did we need to be projected here?"

"Because here we are very close to the goal of our journey and because this is how I've been advised to act."

I looked around at the hard, rocky and arid landscape. I estimated we were at more than four thousand feet in altitude. Gusts of wind swept the valley and the air was very cold, almost nippy. You could not see any pathway and no trace of life except some lichen in what a long time ago could have been a river bed, now completely dried out and full of rugged gravel. From place to place, I could see blocks of ice; and on the slopes around us, the blizzard tousled snow in patches. The landscape looked like a saddle and ahead of us were two grand summits, their peaks covered in snow. It was impressive although slightly hazy.

Strangely, I then felt that my presence there was expected; and I was suddenly overcome by an inner force I could not understand. Intuitively, I connected that formidable state of determination and will I felt within me with the subtle austerity and force that were emanating from the place I was in. Even if the conditions were very hard and unwelcoming at first glance, I still noticed that the landscape had the quality of "cleaning" both the mind and heart; and this subtle purification made room for an intense inner feeling of masculinity, force and virility. This desolate mountainous area, which I initially considered as unwelcoming, was now attracting me like a magnet and generated a heartbreaking nostalgia in me whose source I did not know.

"We must go."

Repa Sundhi's voice sounded strangely close and distinct, even in this very large valley. Startled, I unknowingly gathered my jumper around me. The air temperature, however, was much less colder than it should have been at that altitude and in weather like that. I asked the lama how this was possible.

"This is one of the yidam's contributions. He personally would not need such a facility but thought that we would hold up better in this way."

I looked at the yidam with gratitude. His giant body was perfectly integrated in that landscape, and it wasn't hard at all to believe that a god can easily overcome even the harshest terrestrial conditions.

"Have we been translated in time as well?" I asked, slightly worried. I was wondering if I still had the chance of getting home alright after a spatial translation and that a time translation gone wrong could be fatal.

"No, it wasn't necessary," answered Repa Sundhi. "This doesn't mean it is not possible," he immediately added. "Although apparently distinct, the subtle energies of space and time are intertwined and determine the main characteristics of the surrounding reality. At a certain stage of your spiritual progress, it will be possible for you too to control, at will, these energies. This doesn't happen by chance though but only in a complete agreement with the energetic harmony and balance of that respective area of the universe."

"Still, as far as I know, modern science does not agree with these ideas, at least from a practical point of view," I said.

"This is the drama of the contemporary man of science," the lama said. "Even if he has made some theoretical progress, he tends to over appreciate his efforts and this is a dangerous trait as it limits the freedom of consciousness. Theoretical results and hypotheses can be an incentive but also frustrating. Here, as in many other cases, what is opposing is the vanity of the idea of supremacy. The man thinks he has reached all the way to the top when, in fact, he is only at the beginning of the road."

I was walking carefully through the sharp stones, trying not to cut my shoes in them. We were walking through the valley towards the two peaks ahead of us.

"Is this an area often travelled by others?" I asked, wanting to know if we were going to meet anyone on our way.

Repa Sundhi shook his head for no.

"This mountain is protected subtly. Very few pilgrims have access here and only by the grace of some very high deities. Those two peaks cannot be climbed. The only way to the other side is through a secret passage that few people in the world know. You are on the border between two very different worlds."

"And we are going towards that secret place?" I asked, full of hope and emotions.

"Yes, but you won't cross to the other side — not now. Events need to happen in a given succession in order to ensure a being's historical fluency and, extrapolating, for the entirety of humanity. There's a time for everything, and you will probably also get to know the other land in a not too far away future."

I was a bit disappointed but at the same time slightly confused. With a faint glimmer of hope, however, I asked some questions.

"What is beyond these two peaks? What kind of land is that and who inhabits it?"

Repa Sundhi did not answer me but continued to walk without looking at me. After a little while, I asked again.

"If we are not crossing to the other side, can you at least tell me where we are going now?"

My request was justified as we had already reached the base of the two majestic peaks. Their height was staggering but what was overwhelming was that the rock wall was practically vertical and almost completely smooth without any cracks. I then understood why Repa Sundhi said the peaks could not be climbed. And it was indeed so as they formed an insurmountable barrier.

The lama came to the front of the group and guided us to the right. We then started to obliquely climb the relatively easy incline leading to the base of the gigantic rock wall. Behind us you could almost not see the valley anymore, it being shadowed by a dense fog and twilight. Suddenly, behind a rock, an opening appeared in the mountain's massive rock wall. I stopped as if electrocuted. An obscure but very intense fear overcame me without me being able to determine its real reason. I thought it was because of the mysterious opening in the mountain. The crevice was very narrow, only a little larger than shoulder-width and it seemed completely dark from the outside. Its height was remarkable though, over eight meters. It looked like a cut in the mountain's massive body and suggested the existence of unknown mysteries behind it.

I stopped a few meters from the dark opening in the mountain and asked Repa Sundhi if that was the place of crossing to the other side. He was right next to the entrance and turned to face me before speaking.

"Yes, this is the secret crossing passage, but I have already told you that this will not be your experience for today. You must be patient and have discernment."

The yidam drew near the crevice and waited behind Repa Sundhi. Even he, with his imposing stature, seemed minuscule next to the greatness of that gigantic rock wall.

"Now, just the yidam and I will enter while you two will wait for us here," the lama said. "We won't be long."

With these words, he vanished through the opening, followed closely by the yidam. In order to be able to fit his broad shoulders, the yidam had to enter slightly sideways. All of a sudden, the landscape looked very bare and even threatening. It was very quiet and even the wind was not blowing anymore.

I looked at Elinor. He was calm and did not seem to worry at all, suggesting this was not the first time he had been faced with such a situation.

"Have you followed this trail before?" I asked, hoping to get some support.

"No, not here; but I have been with Repa Sundhi in other similar places: in the Himalayas and the Andes in Peru."

I was looking at him helplessly. I had the feeling that we had been abandoned there forever. In that unknown place, completely isolated from the civilized world, we didn't have too many chances of survival. Panic overcame my mind with the thought that we would freeze to death without shelter and food. Night fell rapidly over the snowed peaks as Elinor and I waited at the bottom of that incredibly tall mountain with no certainty that we would ever be saved. Even if we managed to somehow survive, we would have to reach a Tibetan village lost in the mountains that would lack any modern means of communication or transportation. At best, assuming that I would not be thrown into a Chinese prison, years would pass before getting back home to Romania.

I described my bleak perspective to Elinor but he started laughing heartily and told me that the rarefied air was probably playing tricks with my mind.

"Of course you don't care," I said. "You still have another two thousand years to live, but I would like to use the little time I have left as much as I can."

Thinking lucidly, I realized that he was right. The very strong air, even if rarefied, exacerbated certain mental functions which blazed at the first alarm. This awareness of mine was enough to allow me to return to a normal state of understanding and appreciate the actual situation. I then said to Elinor that I will have to make more journeys of this kind in order to get used to the rigors of the mountains.

While we exchanged impressions on this subject, Repa Sundhi and the yidam came out of the dark opening in the mountain and signaled us to come closer. We got next to the gigantic crevice, but I could not see a thing in the dark. The walls at the entrance were slightly rugged and cut into the mountain rock in the simple shape of a rectangle with its height much bigger than its width. A strong emotional state overcame me as I came closer to the rock wall. I felt there was something enigmatic in there, something profoundly mysterious that I knew nothing about. Repa Sundhi looked at me very kindly and spoke.

"You will now enter this mountain and find all the answers to your questions about the purpose of this journey. This moment is important as it will initiate a series of positive actions in an avalanche by means of an essential trigger that also involves your being. Don't be afraid. We will be with you for a while."

Having said that, Repa Sundhi took my right hand in his left and signalled me to follow him. With my heart in stitches, I entered the unfathomable darkness inside the mountain.

The Sacred Cave

The yidam and Elinor were right behind us. As soon as I entered the niche in the mountain, I could not see anything any-more; but after a few seconds, I realized that the corridor was shaped approximately like an S. In the beginning, it turned to the right and then to the left. When we were on this last bend, I suddenly saw ahead of me, less than three meters away, a huge opening, which was lit. We entered a big cave whose ceiling was a bit taller than the crevice we came through. It was prob-ably ten meters above the floor of that cave.

From the very beginning, I was struck by a special element. The cave was discreetly lit by a very pleasant pale blue light, but I could not see its source. Another aspect that caught my atten-tion was the air temperature. It was almost warm compared to the temperature outside. I found this inviting and the magical sparkle of the stalactites and rock walls was creating a fairy tale background that was amplified by the discreet murmur of crystal pure water. Following the course of that spring, I noticed that it ran through the rock formations on the ground, disappearing under the wall to my right.

The cave advanced into the mountain for a fairly short dis-tance, not more than 10-12 meters, after which it narrowed a bit and bent into a left turning corridor; but from where I was stand-ing, I could not see any other details. That subterranean place was emanating great purity and a certain refinement that I cannot define any better than that. My entire being was enveloped in a delicate emotion, and I felt as if I had been lifted to a superior state of experiencing and understanding. It is fairly hard to describe the very special emotions I was then feeling within the depths of my being, but the most appropriate comparison seems to be to a continuous and very delicate vibration that I could perceive everywhere in my body.

Repa Sundhi advised me to take a few more steps forward while he, together with the yidam and Elinor, remained at the entrance. I walked up to one bigger rock formation which was covered in small quartz crystals that sparkled in myriads of colors. Excited and nervous, I didn't know what to expect. Those next moments seemed as long as hours as an incomprehensible impatience was growing within me. All of a sudden, my heartbeat accelerated and my whole body was enveloped in heat. My mind was pulled as if in a whirl and everything around me seemed to have come closer, spinning at great speed. Then everything suddenly calmed down, and I now felt as if I had just returned from a long journey although my agitation probably didn't last more than a few seconds. I was calm, enveloped in a profound inner peace.

It was then that I saw the goddess. She appeared unexpectedly, coming from the cave's corridor as she slowly advanced towards me. I am well aware that I will never be capable of faithfully describing in words what I felt in those unique moments. We are used to living in a very limited reality which does not give us the much richer and much more nuanced gamut of experiences and sensations of worlds that are superior to the physical plane. The mind of the ordinary man is so contracted to the dimension he lives in and the interests he has that when confronted with a reality exceeding his power of understanding, he has a tendency to block and even refuse what he perceives. Fortunately, as I had already been through such stages in previous situations, I had some experience in these matters. But here, the situation was different.

For the first time in my life, I was meeting a being that was obviously from another world and a world of which I did not have the faintest idea. Even so, I immediately knew that she is a very elevated deity. I cannot explain very well how I knew. It was probably from her unusual appearance correlated with the very intense emotion I felt when I saw her face; combined with the knowledge I had of the oriental pantheon of deities and their iconographic representations. In some way, my subconscious fused all the information to a definite and very clear conclusion. Or perhaps it was a very strong telepathic transmission that determined a profound belief within my being. No matter the reason, I knew I was facing a goddess.

Stunned, I watched as she came closer to me. The feeling I had then was that she was moving slowly, like walking on water, although I could see very well that her steps were on the ground. The closer she came, the more pressure I felt on my body so that it almost pushed me backwards. My heart was racing, and I could feel my blood rushing through my body. Everything around me seemed to be dilating as things became brighter and clearer.

The goddess was stirring. No one could have remained indifferent to her astonishing appearance or resisted her intense look. She was very tall for a woman. I think her body was almost two meters in height but perfectly harmonious. I had never seen something so delightful that illustrated such perfection of form. Even now, when I write all of this, the image of the goddess is so alive in my mind that, just by mentally projecting myself into those extraordinary moments I have lived, I can see everything in the finest detail and exactly as I perceived and lived it then.

Her imposing height was doubled by an extraordinary radiation that she emanated in an almost visible way. I had noticed something similar with the yidam when I saw the air vibrating around his body. Only now, this mysterious radiation was emanating from the body like rays of the goddess although these were not rays of light. It was more of a subtle and hidden vibration, but because of its profoundness, it became much more pervasive. This was probably why that phenomenal force and energy that she radiated was creating the sensation of "pressure" that "pushed" me back.

She was in front of me now, less than a meter and a half away. I was overwhelmed. I raised my eyes and looked at her face, but in that same instant I knew I could not do it. Her dazzling unearthly beauty took my breath away. Those unbelievable eyes pierced my soul and heart to the most hidden depths. I never believed that the beauty of form could have such an impact over a man's consciousness; but I understood very well that it was a combination between the radiation of her aura and the shape of her body and face that embodied perfection. Even so, the impression that her incomparable beauty and purity had on me literally took my breath away. I involuntarily leaned by the rock wall to my left and could barely stop my body shaking. Barely able to breathe, I almost could not open my eyes. Even though there was no light to blind me when I looked at her face, my breath stopped and I felt as if I was fainting. That is why I half-closed my eyes and looked at her only from the waist down.

I know for sure that such a unique experience must be lived in order to fully understand it and to be able to perceive all of its nuances. All descriptions seem poor and insignificant compared to the formidable emotional imprint I lived at the time. The visual and subtle energetic impact of that unearthly being proved to be much stronger than my reasoning. I did not even ask myself whether I was dreaming or having a real experience or if what I was perceiving was verifiable by modern scientific knowledge. The presence of the goddess was so vivid and overwhelming that there was no room in my mind for other ramblings or secondary thoughts. My entire being was filled to the brim with that unmatched sensation of an indescribable beauty from another world.

I know my description cannot even surmise a part of the actual perceptions I had then and that my efforts in this direction will never be enough. I will try, however, to present a few general features that could give you at least an approximate idea of the astounding appearance of the goddess.

She did not look like any of the known human races. Her skin was blue with even some tinges of dark blue and was very smooth and shined sublimely in the reflection of the light and crystals in the cave. This was the main characteristic of her body that shocked the mind right from the beginning. Still, if the mystery emanating from her being would have stopped at that, I think I could have coped quite well in that meeting. But the completely unusual aspect of her skin was greatly amplified by the dazzling beautiful features of her face and, in particular, her divinely celestial eyes. These could be very well likened to two intense flames that subdue everything in their path. What in our eyes is the white part was bright yellow and almost glistening in the goddess. Her iris was dark green. This amazing combination of colors was creating a formidable hypnotic sensation. The brightness of her eyes was amplified by the blue tinge of her skin, but at the same time, the entire face of the goddess was lit by their mysterious incandescent radiation. The sensation given by her eyes was at first so shocking that the feeling was one of paralyzing fear over the entire body. Only then, while still having a gram of lucidity, was I able to realize the depth of compassion and kindness her look actually expressed.

For a few moments, my initial blindness did not allow me to judge things naturally and normally and I was attracted towards my self-limiting feelings of fear and self-preservation. I was, however, helped to surpass that difficult moment in order to have a correct perception of the situation. Incapable of making any move, I was almost suffocating because of the impact the beauty of the goddess was having upon me. I leaned on the massive stone next to me. She then came even closer. As if in a slow motion movie, I perceived details that strongly impinged upon my subconscious. All of my senses were acute and the passing of time seemed to have slowed down. It felt like I was living in a different world, but I was nevertheless very lucid.

I then felt her body heat enveloping me and giving me perhaps the most intense sensation of well-being I had ever experienced. It was like a delicate breeze that seemed to pervade me, neutralizing the psycho-mental contractions I was involuntarily manifesting. At the same time, I perceived the smell emanating from her body. If I had been very pleasantly surprised by the sacred smell irradiated in the yidam's presence, I was shocked by the incredible nuances of her perfume and its extraordinary purity. It was as if thousands of flowers had been gathered there; and still, it was even more than that. It was the smell of a sacred place, of mysteries that cannot be told, of a reality way beyond our world which cannot be described. In a way, it was an intuitive smell, but it did not stay the same for too long but was permanently changing, either as a sublime perfume that was well defined or a combination of olfactory nuances.

This perception completely turned inside out whatever was left untouched in my being. I couldn't explain why it happened like this, but I felt that in those moments that I had totally abandoned myself to the goddess in an impetuous impulse of unconditional love and frenetic adoration. The divine smell of her body, now very close to me, brought out an unexpected baggage of ancestral memories, fragments of undefined sensations, and strange images I could not identify in the course of my life. It was like an explosion of very profound feelings and perceptions were bringing me closer in a mysterious and intoxicating way to that divine being.

I raised my eyes again and looked at her face of rapturous beauty. In order to give you a corresponding analogy from our world, I could say that her features were a combination between those of the European race and the Asian race; but in addition to that, there was something I can hardly define which was not of this earth. The face of the goddess radiated an unequalled nobility and royal bearing; but not in the sense of arrogance and ego but of wisdom and firmness. The proportions of the nose and mouth were perfect and her red lips emanated an almost tangible sensuality. Her fine and delicate smile was revealing the white-ness of perfect teeth and emphasized her cheekbones. The su-perb eyes were big and slightly oblong, and her black eyebrows, slightly arched, defined even better their perfect shape. The long black long hair was falling straight to half-way down her back and was shimmering magically in the blue light of the cave. Her forehead was clear; and in the middle of it, I could see a vertical line of approximately five centimeters that was of a dark violet color and phosphorescent.

I noticed that the skin of her face was a lighter shade of blue while the perfect neck was almost navy blue. Maybe that was just my feeling as a result of the luminous and stirring radiation emanating from her eyes. The goddess was wearing a simple translucent dark green veil that matched the color of her skin and eyes in a remarkable way. This veil was pinned in a compli-cated way over her right shoulder and loosely gathered around her waist with a golden thread. The sheer material the veil was made of allowed a discreet glimpse of the superb shape of her breasts and the shiny dark blue skin of her thighs.

The goddess brought her hand closer to my neck and touched me lightly at the base of it. Immediately thereafter, she made the same gesture to the middle of my forehead and the crown of my head. I could see her delicate fingers very closely with their nails of dark red and her arm stretched in a natural gesture. The gor-geous gold bracelets adorned in rubies that she wore on her wrist were moving slightly and making a bright tinkling noise. On her unveiled upper arm she wore another bracelet of gold, wider and encrusted with sapphires. Her ankles were also adorned in thin gold bracelets, but these had no precious stones. Around her neck she had a necklace of a rare beauty made of emeralds and white pearls that shone brightly in contrast with her delicate blue skin.

The moment she touched me with her fingers, an inner light-ing crossed my body along the spine. I thought I would faint but I did not. I was still standing in the same place, but I could not feel my body anymore. It was as if I had been overcome by general numbness although my mind was very lucid. The predominant feeling I was experiencing then was one of escape, of great freedom. I was small and at the same time very big.

After a few moments, when she touched my forehead, I felt a colossal inner vortex that irresistibly enveloped me and lifted me up higher and higher at a staggering speed. Louder and louder, I could then hear a very elevated vibration that immediately got all of my attention. I could feel that vibration in every atom of my being and had the certainty that it represented something fundamental, a gigantic platform of support. I wanted to leap without any second thought into that ocean of sound that I felt was filling everything, but it was then that the goddess touched the top of my head. A formidable thunder invaded my being at the same time with a white blinding explosion. I could not say if I was in the air or on the earth. I could only see a white light shining like a star above my head. From time to time that star would irradiate multicolored sparks like a rainbow that would face into a space I could not define. Gradually, the white light started to dim, allowing me to again see the details of the cave. In a few seconds, I was back to normal, but the light remained concentrated in a minuscule dot slightly above my head. I could not see it and yet I knew it was there as I could feel its presence as an extremely pleasant cooling sensation coming down to my neck.

I was very close to the goddess and was contemplating her, being aware that only through her will was I able to sustain myself without losing consciousness. That was the moment when she started to talk to me. I will never forget that voice and its extraordinary nuances. There was a great difference between the yidam's voice and what I was hearing now. How can I describe in a credible way a voice that sounds as if it were more than one voice with different tonalities which remains perfectly unitary at the same time? Although the goddess was facing me at less than a meter away and speaking slowly while looking into my eyes, I felt as if her voice was coming from far away and from all directions simultaneously.

Submitting this experience to a second analysis, what I heard was not a human voice. It reached my ears as if each utterance was doubled or tripled, but all these overlappings were delayed only so slightly and had different tonalities so that the overall effect was very strange and unusual. In the beginning, I had the tendency to look around me for the source of the voices I perceived as coming from many different directions, but I soon realized that it was in fact the voice of the goddess. She had a warm tone with many nuances, but I also noticed a slight shrill-like quality akin to a guitar string that is overworked.

Although the words she was saying were in a language unknown to me, I could still, curiously enough, perfectly understand their meaning. Without being too strong, her voice was pervading and instantaneously focused my attention upon her. I watched the movement of her lips in fascination and felt with all of my being the formidable radiation emanated by her body. Barely perceivable, I could see her chest moving rhythmically but very slowly, at one with her breath. At the same time, my mind faithfully registered all the words she was speaking. She told me that my coming there had a very well defined meaning and that it was correlated to everything in a very complex chain of causalities. She explained that in order to be capable of coping with her presence and hearing her voice, a kind of leap of my level of consciousness and energy was needed, a leap that she had induced by touching me with her hand.

The experience you just lived through is a preparation for a special initiation you will receive soon. In a short while, we will meet again and you will then meet other special beings that have also been initiated; but unlike you, they had this experience while dreaming. Not all people face the same kind of experience as this depends on the inner structure of each one of you. This is why they received different types of initiation during their dreams. There is, however, a common ground that ties and brings you all together. There are several groups of people in your country that are guided and helped to evolve in this way.

You must know that this method is also applied to human beings in other areas of the world.

The body and face of the goddess had a fascinating attraction for me. I was almost in a trance as I looked at her perfect beauty and listened to her out-of-this-world words. In a low voice, I asked her a question with profound emotion.

"What is in reality the purpose of these special preparations? Things seem complex to me and the efforts very sustained. What is happening here? What is secretly being planned?"

I then noticed that the vertical violet line in the middle of her forehead intensified its shine. The voice of the goddess then enveloped me from all directions.

"When the time comes, causes that have been long seeded will start to come to fruition. This, however, depends mainly upon people's will. There is never just one possibility, but in the case of major events, we can talk about directions of probability. The true battle is to tip the balance of the most probable direction one way or the other."

The goddess then looked at the trio standing behind me who were next to the gap in the mountain wall. She then exchanged a few phrases with Repa Sundhi in a language I did not understand but assumed was Tibetan. Immediately after that, all three of them left the cave, leaving me alone with that celestial being. It was as if my thoughts were numbed, and I only wanted to look at her and adore her divine beauty and majestic grace. I felt my heart brimming with an uproar that I could not control anymore. Tears filled my eyes and ran down my cheeks. I tried to remain standing although my feet were trembling and my hands were weak.

I then noticed how the eyes of the goddess became brighter. The air around her lit up, pulsing in golden rays like high intensity flashes. She moved further away from me, making a discreet sign to follow her. A few meters from the end of the cave, on the left of the corridor, I noticed an area that seemed cut into the rock. It looked like a giant step or a stage of approximately one meter and a half in height. Its depth was not more than a third of its height.

The goddess stopped next to that area and invited me to come closer. On the flat stone was a sculpted box made of a dark colored noble wood. At her request, I lifted the lid of the box and saw inside a yellow-brown rolled parchment. I took it out of the box and opened it slightly. It was covered in signs made in an ink whose color had become a sort of grey mixed with green. Its color had probably been black initially but with the passing of time, the contrast faded. I noticed that the roll was very old; and even though it looked as if it had been kept in very good condition, the text was hardly visible in some places due to the numerous cracks in the hide that the parchment was made of. The written characters looked like those of the Sanskrit language, but I was more inclined to believe it was a text in Tibetan. I looked inquiringly at the goddess and she spoke.

"It is one of the parchments that were hidden all around Tibet a long time ago. Each of them has its own importance and destiny. The one you are holding now has an essential value, not only due to the contents of the text but also due to the fact that it has been found. Even if this does not seem like much to you, know that it will generate a series of actions and events which will have a very profound impact upon humanity."

I felt as if I had been transported into a fairy tale reality. Nonetheless, I could not deny what I had felt and seen. I asked her what the origins of the parchment were.

"This one and the other ones I told you about contain important initiatory texts and information revealed by the Divine Sovereign Sage of the Three Worlds, the great Guru Rimpoche."

The goddess's voice then took on an even more profound vibration that filled me with a heart rendering feeling of love.

"In his never ending compassion for all ignorant human beings, the divine master presented some fundamental teachings that were written by his most important disciples and then hidden in certain places in Tibet. The parchment you are looking at was written by one of Guru Rimpoche's closest disciples herself. She had the main role of synthesizing the teachings of the great spiritual guide which she organized into chapters and wrote down in scrolls which she hid in secret places."

"Why did she hide it? Why did she act in this way?" I asked, surprised.

The goddess's divine eyes were fixing upon me like two eternal flames.

"Humankind often goes through certain phases of spiritual conditions," she said to me. "The present period is the most bleak and decadent of it all. Those teachings had to be passed on in order to start a new spiritual knowledge of the human. The period in which they were revealed by the great spiritual teacher of Tibet was very troubled and they would not have managed to have a significant impact in a larger area. Their purpose was anticipated over a great leap of time, to the present situation where free and easy communication between people is possible.

"All of this has been predicted in detail; but in order for the action to be successful, the parchments had to be preserved and guarded under the best conditions so that they were not stolen or destroyed. Guru Rimpoche and his disciple gave this responsibility to certain subtle entities that did not allow anyone to come near those respective places except for those who were meant to discover them. The terrible yidam you have met had the task of guarding this secret and hardly accessible place which, furthermore, is a gate to another realm."

In my mind, connections were being made at light speed, but my heart was quivering under the emotion that the goddess's words generated within me. In a very special way, these triggered states and images of those long ago passed times and even of the beings that had acted then. I could not actually see all of those events, but I still somehow perceived some of the scenes in my mind. After they were related to me by the goddess, I knew them and that filled me with unequalled amazement and joy. Without any doubt, I was convinced that this ability had been imprinted on me by her in order for me to be able to believe what I was hearing. This made me again feel a wave of deep gratitude and love which I offered her from all of my heart. Watching me being overwhelmed by new frenetic emotions, she smiled her dazzling smile and spoke to me once again.

"In times to come, you will be confronted with people's opaqueness and fear of knowing and starting out on the spiritual path, but these problems must not become obstacles or barriers in the way of your mission. The teachings in this text and the others, to which you will later have access, must be wisely spread to those willing to receive and apply it in their own life. Many are lazy, and their laziness is chronic. Laziness is actually a dangerous trap of the mind which then contracts and takes the human being away from the surrounding world. Lazy people are helpless, wanting to have everything but in fact have nothing. If they are asked to act, they get upset as they feel chained in their own laziness, like an animal in a cage. Their general feeling is that they are not capable of anything and thus are not interested in what exists outside of themselves. They are the prisoners of their own mind which dictates to them when there is any exterior intervention: 'I can't. I don't want to. I don't have time. I am not interested.'

"Always turn towards those who keep their spirit alive. It is possible that they too might have a thin crust of laziness and inertia in the beginning, but that will give way soon to the subtle heart which, in their case, is awakened."

"What about the others?" I asked. "Why are not the others capable of this comeback?"

"You have no idea yet of the extraordinary force developed by inertia and laziness. It is a type of descendant energy that not only ties the being on a physical level but especially on a psychic and mental one. Deep inside of himself, the lazy one is in fact really attached to the comfort offered by life, by his often phantasmagorical thoughts and the prejudices he does not want to give up. He does not have the capacity of realizing his condition and imagines his life as very good and running normally.

Many find themselves in this deplorable condition. Their time comes when they make great efforts to come out of the torpor they live in."

It was like I was embedded into the magical atmosphere of the cave. The presence of the goddess so close to me, the dazzling perfume that she emanated, and her everlasting look were all creating within me a state which was almost a suspension of body and mind.

"There are many ideas coming to my mind and many questions I don't have answers for," I said. "It is a mystery the way I met you. Your presence is overwhelming."

My words choked me with emotion and I almost could not think coherently anymore. It was as if the area of my head was on fire and my chest was vibrating with energy.

"It is an enigma for you," the goddess said. "For me though, your soul is like an open book. What use would it be for you to know now all the particularities of the situation? The karmic current brought you here without you even realizing it. The parchments containing the secret texts revealed by Guru Rimpoche will have a strong impact over the future destiny of Humankind. Many of them have already been discovered by human beings fulfilling certain karmic conditions. Compose yourself within your soul and understand the significance of your mission."

Having said that, the goddess flashed, lighting the entire cave. Her eyes were shining like two powerful rays and the éclat she emanated was unimaginable. Gradually, the intense light dimmed, and I could see once again the way she looked at me, with great love and kindness.

"Guru Rimpoche himself came to this cave?" I asked, wanting to know in order to understand some of the perceptions I had a few moments before.

"He didn't, but his wise disciple entered here to hide the parchment. That happened a very long time ago. With the divine powers she had, she modelled the stone wall in the shape you are seeing now and placed the wooden box there. This cave is very special because it leads to another world. That is why the text hidden here is also very important. At first, however, only very few people will understand its contents. In it is described the real nature of the attachments that chain man to the world and five very efficient meditation techniques are mentioned in order to help overcome this important obstacle. Finally, the one whose compassion is infinite made some prophecies related to the great transformation that humanity is going to go through. In part, these prophecies refer to your country, too. They can't be fulfilled, however, if an authentic awakening of people towards spirituality is not going to happen.

"The heavy chains that tie these people are, in fact, the attachments and selfishness that are generated by them. Hate, anger and misunderstanding of situations and reality add to the baggage of negative emotions. The ones who manifest it and even cultivate it will be permanently subjected to suffering and deception. For such a man there's a great distance to the clear and pure light of his divine essence, and he will torment himself within the fog of his gross thoughts, full of attachment towards what he wants to achieve without actually getting it. Such a being lives in extremes, being permanently torn between the intensity of pleasure and happiness and the desperation of a dire suffering. He can't have a friend or a lover without strongly attaching to him or her and also can't see an enemy without becoming very angry or even hating him. Never forget that you will only find the profound peace of the soul in the perfect balance between these extremes. No matter if it is ephemeral joy brought about by pleasant situations or the fierce anger unleashed by a hurt ego, these are all just illusory and even demonic influences that digress the human being from his meaning in life.

"When facing the illusions that are often orchestrated by the malefic forces of the Creation, a man is like a domestic animal. He feels good and safe in his master's yard if the master feeds and takes care of him. The domestic animal forgets, however, that it is only a matter of time until his master is going to kill and eat him. It is the same situation when man falls prey to fits of insensate fury and fierce hate that make him decay and reach a deplorable state."

I listened, enraptured by the goddess's words. Their very special sonority created within me a wonderful state that was facilitating a profound understanding.

"What is the solution then?" I asked.

"Strive towards balance in everything you do," the goddess answered. "Always keep yourself in the center. This will allow you to be in the middle of the action and at the same time not to become attached to it. Be firm and balanced in your kindness towards others without wanting to get something in return. Emotional bartering is even worse than deceit. These are the premises of wisdom."

I now had the feeling that I had been there for days, perfecting my spiritual evolution. The never ending emotions, unrest, weakness and amazement that I had been overwhelmed by until then were now being gradually replaced with a feeling of wonderful force and energy that generated a continuous state of inner happiness within me. But just as I was realizing this with great delight, I intuitively perceived that my meeting with the goddess was coming to an end.

Tending to become sad, there is no way I wanted to leave her in order to come back to our world. The goddess smiled her fascinating smile and spoke to me in a slightly rebuking tone.

"See how difficult it is to keep yourself unaffected by sadness and joy, no matter how intense they are? In the exact moment you think you have reached the apex, you immediately discover the ghost of dissatisfaction and suffering. The truly strong one learns to be beyond both manifestations. In a way, you are attached to my physical shape and my presence. Sometimes thousands of years are needed for these traces of attachment to disappear. To your delight, however, I am telling you that you will see me again soon — very soon."

My heart started beating hard.

"Will I come back to this cave?" I asked. "Will you call me again? If it is so soon, I would like not to leave at all. I would like to stay here and maybe Elinor and Repa Sundhi would also want to share this place with me."

After I finished speaking, I looked at the sublime goddess with pleading eyes. She looked back at me in a way that made me burst into tears. It was practically impossible to resist the energetic influx she generated within me. Her face of stirring beauty impressed me so much that my emotions would reach a paroxysm at some moments so that I was not capable of uttering another word. Her divinely harmonious body and the very delicate gestures she was making generated within me, especially when her eyes were on me, a strong tremor manifesting boundless love and compassion. I felt then as if all the waters of the universe were pouring their ancestral mysteries through the light of those divine eyes.

"You do not need to stay here," the goddess said. "Your mind and imagination are too excited now for you to express yourself logically and coherently," she added, smiling more broadly. "It's nothing. As soon as you leave this cave, you will return to a normal state but a much more evolved one than you were used to before."

"If I'm not going to meet you here, then where will I see you again?" I asked.

It was difficult to control the bitterness of the separation.

"It will be in your very own country. Repa Sundhi and the yidam will accompany you there. It is the place that the great sage Guru Rimpoche speaks about in his prophecies contained in the text you found here. He mentions that in these end times there will be a land in the west with a great amount of water next to a triangle of mountains. In those mountains great mysteries are hidden which will be discovered. Goratri is the mountain at whose peak a very important focus of energetic impulse exists.

"The divine master's prophecy states that the no return path of the transformation on this planet will be marked by an extraordinary discovery that will be made in the mountains of your country. This you already know. From now on, all things are closely tied in together and are determined at a very profound causal level. The second important element, generated by the first, is the discovery of this written parchment and bringing it into the world where it will gradually be made known in several stages. You will have a significant contribution in this process which will then trigger a series of beneficial secondary causes."

While she was saying these last few words, the goddess started to distance herself but was still facing me. I was in the same state of confusion as in the first moments when I had seen her. It was a feeling that she was floating rather than walking although it was just a strange optical illusion.

A powerful inner impulse made me jump. It was not possible for her to leave so soon. She could not leave me all alone so quickly! In a few seconds, she disappeared down the corridor at the back end of the cave.

Without paying attention to anything else, I dashed in that direction. The corridor was quite narrow and brightly lit. I walked through it decidedly, but after turning left, I stopped in amazement. After just two to three meters, the corridor ended in the mountain wall as if it had only been dug out to that point. I told myself that there must be a secret door or exit, and I started to look around me, feverishly touching the rock and hoping that I would find the secret opening mechanism of this door. But soon enough, I had to abandon that action as I could very well intuit that it was not going to be successful. I knew that the goddess did not need a secret door or hidden mechanisms in order to cross to different planes. Her quite sudden disappearance, however, almost like her emergence, turned my being inside out and filled my heart with the aching longing to see her again.

My entire energy was then concentrated in a live and intense desire of calling her to come back. I immediately realized that I was behaving childishly; but at the same time, I became aware that I did not know how to call her. Suddenly, my despair had reached a paroxysm. In that very moment, I heard her well known voice in my mind, saying just one name very clearly: Machandi. I froze. The next moment, I spoke her name myself, and I noticed with great joy that its effect was very relaxing and calming. Nonetheless, the impact of her abrupt departure was still very strong and was not going to fade so quickly. The only factor that I considered to be positive in those moments was that, as she promised, I was going to meet her again in a very short time period.

Impatient to find out from Repa Sundhi when that meeting would happen, I went towards the stone step in the mountain's wall and took the wooden box that contained the precious parchment. I looked once more at the cave where I had just lived through what was perhaps the most emotionally intense experience of my life. It then occurred to me that its sacred space and dreamlike blue light had been guarding the secret entrance to another world for thousands of years. I was not meant to know at that time, however, what mysteries that world was hiding or who its inhabitants were. I was almost sure, however, that between that mysterious land and the great discovery in the Bucegi mountains was a very strong connection, and I was hoping that I would have the opportunity to find out more details about this in the not too distant future. Besides, Repa Sundhi had said that I would gain access to these secrets but in a certain matter of time. This thought gave me a feeling of hope and trust in the future as I imagined that I would see Machandi again and be around her always. In those moments I was still not completely aware of the real significance of the event I had lived through in the cave. I brought the box closer to my chest, mentally thanking the goddess for her kindness and stepped into the dark space of the niche in the mountain's wall in order to return to the world I had left earlier.

4

THE SECRET INITIATION

In front of the cave, Repa Sundhi, the yidam and Elinor were waiting for me. The cold wind swept me frontally, bringing me back to a much harsher and tangible reality. The shadows of the twilight were darkening the clouds even more than they were already and the rocky landscape was fully contributing to my feeling of sadness after having left Machandi.

As we walked back on the same path we came on, I was deep in thought and profoundly marked by my meeting with Machandi. Having consideration for my state of mind, the other three were also quiet and composed.

I soon realized, however, that I was not really acting correctly. The experience I had just lived through was supposed to be grounds for joy and exuberance and not for sadness and thoughtfulness. The separation from the goddess was predictable, and I had yet to return to the world where I had a meaning and a purpose to put into practice the teachings that had been revealed to me and to fulfill the secret mission that I had been assigned. I had the parchment as well as certain esoteric information and knowledge, but no plan had been mapped out and there was no precise direction of action to take.

Under such circumstances, I understood that this was not like a company where you outline ways and benchmarks in order to reach a performance goal. If it were like that, situations in life would run as if on automatic pilot which would eventually make the "game" predictable. I only had an idea of what I was supposed to do along with some helping "tools." The rest of it I had to figure out for myself: to adapt and look for efficient ways in which truth and spirituality can reach out to those who want to receive them.

People are different. They behave and understand differently as both their personality and their level of consciousness are distinct. Making certain fundamental truths known to them that could radically change their life and capacities is a very dynamic process that does not rely on just one method. In order to be successful in sharing with others and to be as convincing as possible in conveying a new vision of life, I realized that I first had to profoundly understand these aforementioned aspects of people myself. Fortunately, destiny has facilitated me with the friendship of some exceptional beings who have guided me and continue to do so with much competence in the mysteries of spirituality. One of these is Repa Sundhi.

As I continued to walk from Machandi's cave with my companions, I noticed that Repa Sundhi was walking by my side without interfering with my thoughts. I did feel that his very presence, however, was acting as if it were a silent invitation to clarify what I still did not understand.

"You know, there are some unknown aspects related to Machandi that I would like to find out more about," I confessed to Repa Sundhi. "Her presence overwhelmed me, and I must tell you that my entire being is filled with her image and memory."

The lama smiled discreetly but did not say a word and continued to walk alongside me. I was trying to find the most appropriate words to express what I felt.

"At first," I said, "the shock disoriented me but then I composed myself somehow. I felt like she was helping me to do that, but I wonder if the effect of her appearance was due only to her divine form."

Repa Sundhi's voice roused me as if from a deep sleep.

"Of course this was what impressed you most first of all, but the energetic sensations you felt are due to the formidable auric influence she manifests. You will continue to feel these effects for a very long time henceforth."

"Nonetheless, who is she? When she was next to me, I could faithfully perceive everything that she was saying and admire her unimaginable splendor, but if I wanted to ask her something, I was almost unable to gather my thoughts and focus upon them."

The lama immediately cleared up my quandary.

"You were too shaken in those moments to be able to keep a coherent thinking process going. The difference between her level of consciousness and yours is still too big; and although she helped you to overcome some obstacles, the impact upon your mind and perceptions seems to have been stunning. Of course, Machandi could have caused a temporary spectacular leap of your consciousness to bring you closer to her level, but there would then have been a risk of 'short circuits' happening within your mind. That would have triggered unpleasant side effects and even physical problems as your organic structure is not yet fully prepared to sustain such a strong energetic manifestation. This is why Machandi brought you only to the upper limit that you can now sustain."

"Is she a goddess?" I asked. "Who is she? Even now, after having been through such an unforgettable experience, I still find it hard to believe."

"It is normal. Mental prejudices are still very strong, but you will think differently in a little while. Yes, she is a very powerful goddess, but know that she too has walked the ascendant path of evolution. In her case, a great transformation occurred a few hundred years ago. Before that, she was a celestial feminine entity, a dakini, who accompanied one of the important disciples of the wise Padmasambhava of Tibet."

"I am not yet familiar with the history of Tibet, but I feel very drawn to the stories about the great masters of this place," I said passionately. "Machandi spoke to me about the great Guru Rimpoche whose teachings are in this text that I am carrying."

Repa Sundhi smiled understandingly.

169

"He is one and the same as Padmasambhava. This name is more known in the West, but there are many others in the traditional Tibetan texts that have been used to praise him for a long time. He was a spiritually accomplished being who completely reformed the religion of Tibet. This happened more than twelve hundred years ago. The parchment was hidden in the cave by one of his main disciples who was named Tsogyelma or Yeshe Tsogyel."

I suddenly interrupted Repa Sundhi in order to ask him if she was the one who Machandi accompanied as this would explain her presence in the cave and the connection with the parchment that was hidden there.

"No, the goddess has been with another very important disciple of the great sage named Tashi Kyidren. Although she was a princess, she dedicated her entire life to spirituality. In fact, Tashi Kyidren was the embodiment of a dakini and Machandi accompanied her everywhere.

"The goddess you met is much older, from a time which historians still do not know too much about. She was the companion of Rama and his beautiful wife, Sita, after they retreated to the mountain forests. These are from times so old that people consider these stories as legends. There have been more than nine thousand years since, and it is only natural that major errors of interpretation of the reality of those times have occurred, errors that have been transmitted for millennia and through various civilizations up to the present time.

"The so called legend of Rama and Sita that Westerners know from the Hindu epic *Ramayana* is in fact very real. I can even tell you that certain events and facts that we have faced have a direct connection to those times. Machandi, who then lived at the terrestrial level in the very physical projection you witnessed, was a very young dakini who was devoted to that extraordinary divine couple. She could give you some very important details, but this depends upon you as it involves you progressing enough to become very close to the goddess. And, when you reach this level, there won't be any need of her telling you anything as you will be capable of seeing and even 'living' those times yourself in the most real way imaginable."

The thought that I could always remain by Machandi's side was giving me wings.

"The main problem is that, through time, the impression was created that Rama and Sita left current day India and went west when, in fact, Rama actually ruled the present territory of your country," the lama continued to explain. "Much more precise information I can give you is that his royal abode was in the area of Salaj County and that, for several years, he and Sita had a retreat in the mountain forests that was located exactly in the valley of the Apuseni Mountains that we passed through yesterday. There are not many differences from the landscape back then except that the vegetation was much taller. Those were times during which certain deities of the celestial planes were materializing in the physical plane and living for years amongst the people."

Seeing the ever growing astonishment written all over my face, Repa Sundhi continued to tell me of the other extraordinary aspects of those long ago passed times.

"The level of consciousness of the population then living in the Carpathian area was very elevated. People were few and settled mostly in the valleys and on the mountain peaks. Their life was profoundly meditative; and back then, many events happened that today would be categorized as being amazing divine miracles. You must also know that the subtle impregnation of those times was so strong that it still has not completely vanished even today after more than nine thousand years. A fundamental energetic matrix was created then that will be actualized again in the near future as a result of certain laws of cycles.

"There is, of course, much more to say about that long gone era even if scientists affirm that it is just the result of a lavish fantasy. There are, however, some important proofs that some historians possess as well as some remarkable studies that certify the realities I am telling you about. Unfortunately, there are even more researchers who do not want the present idea and conception of how the world evolved to be modified. For them, this would be synonymous to a disaster, both financially as well as geopolitically. It is surprising though that, as far as I know, a very bitter battle against these realities has been fought by some of the historians and academics in your country. Nevertheless, everything will work in such a manner that the truth will soon be revealed."

After a short break, Repa Sundhi continued.

"Rama and Sita's history is slightly more complicated than was described in the Ramayana although the essence of the message has remain unaltered. For example, the interventions and backstage fights of some of the advanced civilizations that existed then, as well as the unimaginable technology developed by them, have been described only sketchily and often in an allegorical manner. Even more, Machandi's presence by Rama's side, after the kidnapping of Sita by Ravana, was intentionally taken out of the story so that it did not create confusion regarding the chastity of the divine couple. Back then, Machandi had been a major contributor to Rama's final victory, and she is also the one who saved Sita from a difficult situation during the last stage of the war which also involved three instances of atomic deflagration. This history, however, is nothing more than a series of stories in the eyes of modern science. We must not pay too much attention to their opinion on such matters as the ignorance and interests of modern researchers leads in other directions than the truth.

"In the area of the Apuseni Mountains where we were transported to Tibet, a space-time portal was created in those times that Rama often used to project himself to different places on the planet. All that was needed was for me to reactivate the energetic plane so that the effect appeared once more, and thus you met the goddess. Accumulating immense experience in manifestation, Machandi always evolved, and at present, she governs a big part of our galaxy and has a superior place in the hierarchy of celestial entities. I know this is almost incomprehensible for you right now, but after you become more familiarized with the particularities of the subtle worlds, you will understand this perspective much more easily."

I was enraptured by the mysteries the lama was revealing and barely felt the coldness of the wind.

"But how is it possible for her to know all that happens in a gigantic volume of space and time?" I asked, overwhelmed by the thought of the amplitude of such a possibility.

Repa Sundhi explained patiently.

"You want to understand this aspect while still on the same level of logic and perception you have now. Consciousness, however, is multidimensional and it evolves over time. The ordinary human lives his life in segments: family, job, business, fun and many more. When he wants something and gets involved in that segment of life, he almost completely forgets about the other ones but they keep on existing. This approach is partial and very limited. The range of human emotions is supported by this very type of fragmented vision upon life that is at the basis of the false idea of who we really are. You erroneously identify with the specifics of one fragment of your life and then feel the need to attach yourself to it. This creates dependency which will turn into frustration. In turn, frustration will inevitably lead to suffering. It is a chain that man scrupulously ties himself to throughout his entire life.

"If you have a larger perspective, however, all aspects of your existence will be perceived as sequences correlated and linked at a causal level. Furthermore, from such a superior position, you will be able to understand all that surrounds you even if it does not involve you directly. This is the fundamental difference between an ordinary human and a sage. In the wise man's case, the expansion of his consciousness can become gigantic whereby it then includes not only what exists within those limits but also makes him capable of directing at will any action or intervention within that space-time frame.

"I think you now understand quite well Machandi's power of influence within the universe. In order to efficiently master and control a high level of manifestation, know that it is necessary that you are also on a superior level to the plane you want to control. A blind man will never be able to lead another blind man."

I understood that condition very well, but I was not yet clear on the cause of the manifestation of our limited emotions that generate suffering. I also did not know the reason why man prefers to segment his life into different bands of interests and actions.

Repa Sundhi then clarified one of the most important aspects of our life.

"The main cause is the wrong idea that man gets about the diverse aspects of his life. Although everything changes and transforms around him every moment, he strongly believes that things and situations can remain the same: unchanged. But, if you analyze this concept profoundly, you will discover that it is completely unrealistic and even lacking logic. Nothing of what surrounds you or exists in Creation ever stays the same, but it always transforms in a continuous evolutionary movement. Can you honestly say that the relations you had stayed the same or that those you presently have will not change? Do you think that the wealth and material possessions that some people avidly gather represent something stable and eternal? By the opposite, in just one moment they can lose everything that they saved for their entire life. The psychological state is not any more stable. When criticized, man gets upset. When suffering any kind of loss, he gets angry. When he doesn't have what he wants, he becomes jealous or envious. All these attitudes are nothing else but negative emotions that compel him to do certain actions. These get 'imprinted' in his personal karma and will generate big problems in his future lives.

"The wrong idea that things or situations are permanent and will never change is the very root of man's suffering. As I was telling you, his vision upon this is completely unrealistic. The true drama is that, although confronted numerous times during his life with situations that refute this conception, he stubbornly persists with this idea. Imagining that nothing changes and what he gets in this life will last forever or will remain the same for him, at least while he's alive, the more the man attaches himself to relationships, feelings, emotions, money, possessions or pleasures. Follow closely this psychological negative manifestation that is attachment. Through the very example given by your own life, you will understand very quickly that it creates expectations, claims and illusions within you. Most often, these are not fulfilled or satisfied and thus suffering appears which in turn generates certain negative thoughts. These will contribute to the negative karma of that respective person and so on, like in a vicious circle. Now you know the chain of man's limitation within Creation. Break this chain and you will be free."

I very well realized that this advice was the cornerstone of my spiritual evolution. It was not very clear to me though how I could eliminate the false idea of the permanence of things. I asked Repa Sundhi to enlighten me in regards to this, and he said the following.

"Everything that is around us and inside our being, no matter if we are talking about the physical organism or the mental and psychic processes, changes continuously but still appears as if it were constant and unchangeable. This is mainly due to our lack of attention on the one hand and to the mental denial of understanding this truth on the other. This is why people become sad or upset when their expectations are not met. Manifesting a will worthy of better things, they keep on persisting with the false idea that maybe things will stay the same, unchanged. In reality, their wild desire only expresses the strength of the attachment which makes them cling almost desperately onto what they imagine belongs to them and do not want to lose. It is clear that this is not possible as it was based on a completely false idea from the start. But, some people are so rooted in their attachments that, in order to keep them at any cost, they prefer to create certain types of ideals whose nature they do not really understand. These goals in life, whether they regard love, art or professional activity, are used only as a shield to hide – from themselves as well as others – their own attachments and possessiveness. However, this genuine psychological and mental "construction" is false and only serves to shadow even more the correct understanding that respective person should have of the nature of things within Creation.

"The only way of breaking this vicious cycle is to lucidly observe the real situation and understand its profound mechanisms. This careful analysis must be done during your daily activities when you are confronted with those very tendencies as well as in silence, when you are on your own, where you can meditate over your actions throughout the day which demonstrate the falsity of your conceptions. If you will perseveringly realize this, the roots of your attachments and inner convulsions will be gradually destroyed.

"Attachments that are kept for a long while transform into habits, meaning that they put down a solid foundation into a man's psycho-mental structure. These are harder to remove in principle, but the method is the same. There are no miraculous pills or magic recipes to cure one of the serious disease that is attachment. You will need to make intensive efforts and support yourself with what you have in order to manage this. Everything a man has tied, he also has to untie."

"OK," I said. "Assuming I will behave in this manner, what will come out of it?"

Repa Sundhi smiled kindly.

"It is best for you to convince yourself. My explanations would be of no real use. It is important to understand, however, that once you get rid of the burden of attachments, the freedom of your spirit, mind and body will be incomparable with any other situation in life. This will then generate within you true happiness without object, meaning that it doesn't depend upon something or someone in particular. You are simply happy because you exist, and everything around you exists simultaneously.

"A direct effect of this inner awareness will be the desire to altruistically help those who need support and to do only virtuous action. Of course, this does not guarantee that you won't ever be faced with problems or states of suffering along the evolutionary and spiritual path that you are following. You must understand that these factors will keep on cropping up for a while due to the fact that the physical and psycho-mental structure is not yet purified; and certain karmic elements which are a consequence of the bad deeds of the past have yet to reach a stage where they must be balanced out. In such situations, your heart should not be gripped by despair and your spiritual practice should not be interrupted. More than ever, that is the time when you need to prove your willpower and perseverance because, as I already told you, everything is fleeting, even the karmic sufferings. Gradually, due to the positive transformations in your life and to the correct manner in which you think and act, these sufferings will diminish more and more and you will gain access to planes of consciousness much superior to the one you are on now."

Having said that, Repa Sundhi stopped walking and signalled us too to do the same. I noticed that we were in the Tibetan rocky valley we had been translated to a while before. The lama then closed his eyes for a few moments while being very still. I was admiring his facial expression of profound focus and inner absorption. It was almost dark outside, but even so, the mountain peaks were mysteriously radiating a diffuse and phosphorescent purple color. All of a sudden, I felt overcome by a strange inner tremor that caused me a slight sensation of nausea. In great amazement, I then saw how the landscape seemed to have 'curved' at the extremities, like undulating waves. Then, we were suddenly inundated by strong sunlight in a clear sky. The translation had happened the other way around, and we were now back in the Apuseni Mountains, close to the great clearing at the top of the hill we had climbed. This time, however, Repa Sundi had achieved our projection directly and wit

177

resorting to the intermediary stages I had witnessed before. I noticed, however, that something didn't seem quite right. I knew that the previous translation had happened in the afternoon and I expected that, after the four to five hours we had spent in Tibet, it would have been evening if not night time. Instead, I could see that it was a bright and warm November morning, and this confused me a bit. I remarked that it should be a totally different time of day.

"That's what it would be if the time had passed according to your subjective impressions," the lama answered. "Meeting Machandi, however, involved slight changes in the space-time continuum so what seemed like just a few hours to you, in reality, lasted much longer."

"Seventeen and a half hours," said Elinor, consulting his watch and calculating the time difference. "So, we have a twelve to thirteen hour discrepancy to objective time."

I don't know why, but I was delighted when I was confronted with the unusual phenomena involving the distortion of space and time. Nevertheless, I still asked Repa Sundhi if this had any secondary effect for the physical body. He explained that there are no dangers in this and that the ideas and assumptions of those in scientific circles are erroneous, mainly due to a lack of experience in the matter.

"The only effects that can manifest are psychic ones as the respective person can be perturbed by the total change in the reality he was used to and of the laws of physics he knew. But even this feeling is quickly dimmed by a very efficient self-adapting mechanism. Nonetheless, in the case of time travel, the issues are more complex."

We soon arrived at the car where we had a light meal. Before starting out on our return journey, the yidam disappeared. Repa Sundhi, however, assured me that I would meet him again in a couple of days when we were to leave for another place in the mountains. As far as I understood, that was going to be an ampler action. The lama then gave me some more details, probably considering that I had by now achieved an important stage in the evolution of my capacity to understand.

"Goratri Mountain, which is mentioned in the prophecies of the great sage Padmasambhava, is in fact Godeanu Mountain, the present name being a natural transformation of the initial one through the past millennia. This mountain is very important in the local energetic balance and also keeps some secrets that will astound the world. Machandi picked that place for a reason."

I was no longer surprised that the lama knew very well what I had talked about with the goddess; but I was very enthusiastic at the news that, in a short while, I would see her again in the mountains that she had spoken to me about. Repa Sundhi told me that we would travel there in a week's time. Until then, he had to dictate to me the translation of the text that was written on the parchment and sort out other aspects related to the trip. He told me that he first needed a few days to understand the text and the words written on the parchment which had been affected by the passing of time.

"It is an old Tibetan dialect which has not been spoken in centuries. I will have to consult certain secret sources of information," he explained.

We reached Bucharest that afternoon without any troubles, and we established that we would meet in four days time at Elinor's villa. I spent that time analyzing my recent experiences and trying at the same time to put into practice the teachings of Repa Sundhi and the goddess. In just a few days, I had seen, known and lived what can usually take years or even several successive lives. I have thus personally convinced myself of the validity of the saying that the year does not bring what the moment can. This was an extra clue for me that transformation will soon happen at all levels and everywhere around the world. Besides, that this is a generally known fact is also played down and trifled which diminishes the strength of the message and tends to shrink people's responsibilities in the matter. Things must be looked at objectively however. No one can deny the serious problems that humanity is currently faced with, but only few understand the hidden causes and their propagation mechanism. This is why people try to superficially solve the situation and forget the fact that their personal problems are the problems of Humankind and are reflected by it. Plus, there is the raging battle of certain occult organizations that are caught up in manipulating and controlling the population's ideas and tendencies which only complicates things even more.

I wanted to responsibly take upon myself a positive role in this fight where good and truth always triumph, and I was very happy that there are beings who can competently guide me in the right direction. That is why, when I met with Repa Sundhi in order to work on the translation of the Tibetan text, I was very resolute and decided to follow the path of spiritual accomplishment.

"It is very well to act like this," said Repa Sundhi. "But do not forget that beforehand you must be firmly rooted in the knowledge of certain laws and fundamental principles of the Creation without which there cannot be any real progress or transformation of your being. There are many connoisseurs of the spiritual aspects, sacred texts and esoteric notions, but their knowledge is relatively dry as it is not doubled by a profound inner realization of what they know."

I agreed with Repa Sundhi as I also knew that the power of words and the righteousness of actions come only from the practical realization of spiritual truths. Every step of spiritual progress is, in fact, a new superior level of understanding the universe and of being able to act efficiently at that specific level.

"The true spiritual teachings are gained with practice," the lama continued to explain. "The process of learning is interactive and man perfects himself in the very moment he correctly applies all the knowledge he has gathered until then."

Repa Sundhi then detailed some ways I could use to control my mental and emotional influxes and also offered me some advice regarding the principles of a healthy life and behavior. He insisted on the importance of applying this knowledge in daily activities as it is only then that they can truly contribute to our evolution as human beings.

"You must not analyze the spiritual books and texts only from an intellectual point of view," he advised me. "It is much better to meditate a little every day upon the truths that are presented in them and then observe the reflections of those truths in your life. Some people get lost in 'sophisticated' analyses and sterile arguments that achieve nothing but the amplifying of their ego as so-called connoisseurs of the esoteric. In reality, they have reached a dead end; and in a way, get drunk on water thinking that they are valuable and even wise. They become arrogant and imagine that they are the only competent keepers of some occult secrets and knowledge, defying, more or less justified, any other opinion on the matter. Often, they even have wrong ideas or lack the understanding of important aspects of spirituality due to either a misinterpretation or the sources of information they consulted which are often incomplete or not genuine. Do not let yourself get caught in the net of such discussions that may seem savant as they will be to no avail. Those who claim to be 'in the know' or 'men of letters' often have more problems and character flaws than simple but honest people who have a pure heart. This is why — I repeat — it is very important to correctly apply the spiritual teachings in your daily life as only in this way will you progress and gradually eliminate your negative karma."

In the three days left until our leaving, I translated the Tibetan text, deciphered by Repa Sundhi, from English. This was not an easy task as some technical terms had no equivalent in Romanian. They were already approximated in English but the lama particularly insisted that I convey in the translation, as much as possible, the spiritual nuances of those expressions. Painstakingly patient, the lama elucidated some profound significance to me by means of comparative examples and many other details so that I could understand exactly what the text refers to and reproduce it accordingly. Finally, I was satisfied with the end result and the fact that I had finalized an important first stage of my mission.

The seventh day after meeting Machandi, I left with Repa Sundhi and Elinor towards the Godeanu Mountain. This time, we started our journey in the afternoon as the lama said that it would be important to arrive there at night. I was starting to get used to such trips and was very happy that I was going to see Machandi again. The week that had just passed since my separation from her had basically been an extension of the emotions I had lived through in the Tibetan cave except that they were refined and much more profound.

I was aware that I had reached a certain stage of maturity and understanding with regard to the amazing experience I had been confronted with and the knowledge that had been shared with me. The last two weeks of my life had been like a tsunami with regard to my emotional knowledge and experience, but I felt like months had passed as I had assimilated a substantial baggage of spiritual information. The strange dilatation of time that I perceived was probably in connection with a subtle action of Repa Sundhi or maybe of the goddess, but I never raised the matter. It is also possible that my perception was due to an inner thoroughness and a penetration into the mysterious layers of self-consciousness that are beyond space and time. I will probably have knowledge of and an answer to this sometime in the future.

I felt well prepared and was anticipating with interest the events that were soon to follow. As usual, the lama did not offer too many details, simply saying that we would climb the peak of a very important mountain which is also a true energetic center of the country. He told me that the peak is called Gugu and that the goddess would manifest herself that night near that peak. Repa Sundhi also said that we would meet a group of people who would share the same destination as us.

"It will look like a mountain trip, but in reality, it will be a true initiation into the subtle worlds," the lama said.

I did not say anything else, preferring to interiorize and thus prepare myself for that event.

When we eventually reached the foothills of the mountain, the night was falling. The weather was gorgeous, but the air was quite crisp. In the jeep, we climbed up a very uneven mountain road for quite a while. At a crossroads, Elinor parked the car and we started to walk up the slope in a perpendicular direction to the one we came from. As I felt myself getting close to the final goal of our journey (my meeting with Machandi), my mind was becoming more and more agitated and I became more and more impatient. I was trying to control myself but my exterior attitude did not fool Repa Sundhi.

"Your impatience can transform into disappointment. I am not saying this is how it is going to be but just raising a possibility. What will you do then? How will you solve the problem? Your mind will probably give you a series of explanations which will not convince you. You will then try to fill the emptiness in your soul with other thoughts or actions, but these will generate, in turn, new effects and more new effects beyond that. You will never see the end of it this way."

I was walking slowly on a narrow path without making too much effort. As always, Repa Sundhi had perceived my inner state very well. I did not know what to say to him.

"You must cultivate your patience," he then said. "It is a quality that very few people have as it involves great self-control and mental maturity. I think you realize, for example, that I am not talking about the patience needed to wait for your turn to pay at a cashier's desk in a supermarket and also not the patience of waiting in line to buy tickets. I am referring to a much more profound attitude of a being which relates to the capacity of controlling certain negative tendencies and impulses. One of the main differences between an ordinary man and a sage is that while the first gives free rein, often without any discernment, to his chaotic and destructive inner tendencies that manifest noisily and even violently, the sage never behaves in this manner. With his balanced attitude, he often manages to calm down the terrible rages of those around him."

"Well, the science of psychology says that you should let go of the inferior inner feelings as otherwise frustrations and tensions in the psycho-mental structure are going to appear," I intervened before suddenly shutting up.

At a more profound level, I was starting to understand that something was not quite right with the conception I had just mentioned. I was thinking that if someone followed this method of "letting it all out," there is no reason to believe that the person would ever reach the bottom. To the contrary, he will become accustomed to the states of fury and anger which by then would be considered natural and recommended and thus create dangerous karmic chains.

"Your reasoning is correct," Repa Sundhi agreed, after I told him how I felt. "The manifestation of anger always attracts the manifestation of aggressiveness which can be more or less obvious. Modern psychology's recipe is false as the ones who circulated it did not profoundly understand what happens at the subtle level of the mind when a man becomes angry or what the karmic consequences he attracts are every time he behaves like that.

"First of all, the lack of control makes him psychically vulnerable even if he then imagines that he crashes everything around him, thus showing strength, domination and power. This is an infantile and egotistical idea. In reality, the furious one unconsciously perceives his weakness, and this is exactly why he tries to make up that deficit with a false impetus. You know very well that such people forget themselves and everything surrounding them while living those moments of fury and become totally absorbed in the destructive state that's overcoming them. They then almost completely lose their lucidity and the logic of their thoughts, not wanting anything else but to impose their own point of view at any cost. This maleficent energy pushes a human being to commit evil deeds; and even if he manages to somehow control himself and not act in this way, unleashed fury can annihilate all the effort that has been made up to that point to

184

control those chaotic states that trouble the mind and the organism. As you can see, it is all a matter of control."

"And to learn how to achieve this control needs a lot of patience and perseverance," I said. "For example, it is clear that if the fury is controlled then the speech and ways of acting will be controlled, too. But you have to know that I wasn't furious at all. I was becoming anxious and feverish in my desire to see Machandi again."

"I know this very well," the lama answered. "I was just suggesting a possible subject of meditation that can be applied in any situation. For example, you could understand from it that patience is closely related to a constant effort. Of course, I am referring to elevated aspects of effort, not necessarily to that of a physical nature. So, I mean the effort of being persevering, the effort of unselfishly helping others and so on. And no matter how strange it may seem, the greatest effort is the one of firmly rooting yourself in meditation."

I admitted to Repa Sundhi that he had hit the spot.

"Yes, there's a problem here," I said. "I tried to do this as well as I possibly could, but it is very difficult. Some people have even told me that they would get bored to death by staying still in the same place for more than a few minutes. I confess that this inhibited me somehow."

"Those who think like the people you mention have a weak and very agitated mind. Don't pay them too much attention as they do not know much of these mysteries. Do not let yourself be influenced by such as otherwise you will always fall into the temptation of taking the easy but descendant path of the ignorant ones. If you are firm in your decision, you will never fail to make progress. While others will struggle with all kinds of problems and sufferings, you will gradually become almost intangible to such difficulties as you will be putting your life in order and balancing your destiny through your positive actions."

"What do you call a positive action?" I asked. "I mean, except for the virtues known to all, I am asking you so as to know if, for example, daily meditation is a positive action. If that is the case, please explain why."

I was paying very close attention to what the lama was telling me.

"Many consider meditation to be a waste of time. Even more, in their never ending stupidity, some associate it with mental alienation or brain washing. In reality, meditation – the same as prayer – is an absolutely necessary aid in order to come away from the surrounding world's agitation and to find yourself in an infinitely expanded state in which the universe you are in now is only a very small part. This is why, when correctly done, meditation practically becomes the most positive and efficient of all actions as it 'adjusts' the existential asperities and makes you profoundly understand life's complicated aspects. Those who do not know this and do not bother to look at things from this perspective live chaotically and at the mercy of fate. After all, meditation allows you to control your destiny. The habit of daily meditation is the only one that the mind needs. All other habits must be eliminated as they create attachments."

It was already night time and we were going up at a steady pace through small boulders and rocks. Paying attention to Repa Sundhi's explanations, I looked down as I walked. When I raised my eyes, I had the pleasant surprise of noticing the yidam who had probably joined us a while ago. He was a few meters in front of us and was guiding us in the right direction. I could see his giant stature perfectly outlined in the moonlight, climbing tirelessly towards the stony peak of the mountain.

Looking a bit ahead and over the yidam's shoulder, I thought I saw a few people gathered together and sitting on the ground. At first, I thought I was wrong; but after only a few meters of walking faster in order to check this out, I convinced myself that there was a group of people waiting in silence. I mentioned this to Repa Sundhi, and he said that he knew about those people, adding that they would accompany us on our way to the top.

We reached the group, and I was surprised to see that it was made up of only young boys and girls. In my estimation, they were all between twenty and twenty-five years old. Being close to them, I notice that all of them were beautiful, well built and harmonious. I immediately realized that they were special beings and much more mature than their age. As we got closer, they got up, looking at us inquisitively.

"Each of them has, in one way or another, subtle karmic connections to these places and have achieved special merits in their previous existences," Repa Sundhi whispered to me while Elinor assured them that we were the ones they were expecting and asked them to also follow us. "Their minds and psyches are ready for the events to come, and they themselves will play an important role in the amazing transformations of this nation. Their presence here is due to successive initiations they have received from Machandi during dreams. She is the one who told them the time and place to come, but in order to convince them, she had to appear in their dreams several times. Such actions are rare but very important."

I counted nineteen people. They were climbing after us in small groups and rarely talked amongst themselves, and when they did, it was monosyllabic. Something was not right, however, as the yidam's presence did not provoke any reaction from them. I was then struck by the thought that while I could still see it, the yidam was invisible to those youths. Repa Sundhi had explained how this could work the very day I met him at Elinor's. Whispering my thought to him, he confirmed it.

"It was not the time or place for them to have this experience with the yidam. It would have troubled them too much. For the initiation that is about to occur, they need to keep a certain state of calm and inner balance."

I was pleasantly surprised by the state of unity manifested by that group, especially as its members did not know each other beforehand. I perceived them as very responsible in regards to their mission. They were serious and dedicated to

187

succeeding although none of them knew what was to come. While I was thinking about this, I noticed a narrow column of diffuse white light through some trees that we were passing. This column of light went from the ground to the starry sky. I lit the area up with my flashlight as it was only six to seven meters away, but I could not see anything out of the ordinary. I left the group and quickly covered that distance in order to investigate the phenomena. It was very strange. The column of light, no bigger than five centimeters in diameter, was coming out of the ground and going towards the sky. As it was diffused and of weak intensity, it could pass unnoticed from far away. Straining my eyes, I then saw that there were many more other luminous columns that were higher up on the mountain towards our left.

I caught up with Repa Sundhi and told him about the strange manifestation. He said that peak Gugu hides many mysteries, thousands of years old, and that they will be partly discovered very soon. The lama confessed that there is a formidable source of energy in the underground of that mountain but did not want to give any other details. I instinctively looked towards the peak, and at that exact moment, a very cold and strong wind hit us from the front and made us wobble. We stopped for a moment; but Elinor, who knew the area, explained that such sudden "out of the blue" manifestations are a characteristic of this mountain. Nonetheless, I was a bit uncomfortable as the cold air current seemed to have brought something else as well, something threatening and unpleasant. Looking again into the darkness above the peak, I was dumbfounded to notice how rapidly it had been covered in black with threatening clouds now rolling in with a dull and distant rumble.

The next moments and the phenomena associated with them occurred in my consciousness progressively but at a slower rate of perception than what is considered normal. I then perceived everything from a state of "suspension" without being able to explain the sudden way everything appeared.

While I was rather worriedly watching the sky that was quickly being covered and foretold of a terrible storm, I was shocked by the extremely powerful lighting that came from the rolling clouds and hit the very top of the mountain's peak. The noise was stunning, shaking our very being.

From that moment on, I saw everything unfold slowly and very precisely. Each sense was sharpened to the maximum and the sensations I felt were very intense. I saw the blinding brightness of the giant lighting spread all the way down the mountain; and even further away, a violet and purple flow that was creating a strange unearthly impression. In the same moment, I saw, a little to our right and higher up, a sheepfold with animals nervously moving around in their enclosure. But what really frightened me as I looked at that almost unreal landscape were three giant sheep dogs that were ferociously coming towards us in huge leaps. Those animals were unusually big and fierce, and their enormous fangs seemed to flash in a demonic grin. What made the deepest impression upon me were the extraordinary leaps they were taking. These leaps were impossible even for a gazelle. Even more, the height they reached while in the air was inconceivable for guard dogs no matter how well trained. I had no illusions regarding the intentions of those frightening apparitions, but the slow motion unfolding of their movements, as I perceived it within my consciousness, allowed me to pay attention to the other members of the group before being overtaken by sheer panic.

I watched Repa Sundhi who was still and facing towards the peak. He seemed to be completely extracted from that landscape and focused in a different direction. Elinor was slowly straightening himself and turning his head towards the advancing dogs. At that point, the yidam took a step sideways in the direction they were coming from and stretched his right hand with an open palm in a gesture of stopping the action. I saw how the air around him started to sparkle as it radiated a phosphorescent white light. Gigantic and terrible in his looks, he would have frightened anyone.

The dogs stopped rather suddenly, but they continued to bark wildly from a distance of some fifty meters from us. They were thrashing and squirming but could not go beyond that fifty meter limit. The brightness of the light was diminishing gradually now and creating strange shadows in the valley. When darkness surrounded us once more, I could not see anything. Even so, I could just about make out what could be the sheepfold higher up the mountain. A heavy silence had come down, interrupted only at times by the thunder rumbling from far away.

I then became aware that I had returned to the normal perception of the events around me. While we kept on going up the mountain, I came closer to Repa Sundhi and told him in short what I had witnessed just moments before. He answered that my perception had been mainly at a subtle level. The fierce dogs were in fact embodiments of astral demonic entities who wanted to attack us and provoke an intense state of fear in order to stop the normal unfolding of the initiation that was going to happen that night. In physical reality, however, the nineteen youngsters did not see or hear anything except the terrible lighting that fell upon the Gugu peak. The lama revealed that I was capable of having those perceptions through the grace of the goddess Machandi who was going to reveal herself very soon.

Meanwhile, our group reached an area where the slope became much more abrupt and rocky. The sky was now completely covered in thick clouds, often pierced by lightning that partially brightened the landscape. The atmosphere was very charged with electricity and the tension in the air was almost tangible. The sky looked like a pot ready to boil over. Two giant lightning bolts hit the mountain slope signalling the unleashing of a great storm. The rain started to fall in heavy waves while the wind raged wildly, spraying raindrops in all directions.

I was then witness to an extraordinary phenomenon. Our whole group was draped in a sort of light that covered and completely isolated us from the terrible atmospheric phenomena that we were surrounded by. The lightning intensified and hit the ground very close to us. I saw blasts of rain stopping at the limit of the diffused light that was enveloping us as in a protective shell.

At Repa Sundhi's direction, we all sat down. I then had an intuition that our protection was created by the yidam who was sheltering us from nature's wrath. I could see around me an almost unbelievable manifestation of atmospheric force and energy. Shrubs were flying through the air, water whirls were fiercely hitting the trees, and there was terrible lighting that was triggering apocalyptic thunders.

In the middle of all of this frightening chaos, I noticed in amazement how the stone of the mountain in front of us, which was at a distance of approximately twenty meters, was gradually becoming transparent, revealing a great cave inside the peak. Surrounded by a magnificently bright aura, Machandi advanced from inside of the cave to the stone wall and outside of it. My heart almost stopped with all the emotions I felt. The radiation of the goddess was now much stronger then than when I perceived it in the sacred cave in Tibet's mountains. Her glorious brightness seemed to cancel the storm outside. The thunder was weaker, the lightning was less and the wind seemed to have vanished, all bowing to the phenomenal greatness that Machandi was manifesting. From her sublime body, rays of multicolored light were radiating like a rainbow, glittering brightly in all directions.

That divine vision shocked us all. None of us were capable of talking anymore, having been left ecstatic and breathless in front of that wonderful apparition of the goddess. Even I, who had some experience with this sort of thing, was really overwhelmed by the intensity of it all. Her beauty and divine grace created within my heart an intensity of happiness that I could barely stand. A few of the boys and girls in the group fell to the ground crying. I was still, blind, and deaf to everything around me, keeping my eyes only on Machandi. The only thing I wished for was to be closer to her and to accompany her in the world she was coming from.

I then noticed that the goddess was not advancing by stepping on the ground but by staying in the air with a majestic grace. Due to the difference in height between the cave and ground level, she was in a plane above our heads as she stopped at approximately ten meters away from our group. Had she come any closer, she would probably have blinded us with the brightness she emanated. As she lifted her hands at shoulder level with her palms facing upwards, I could see how the clouds above us were breaking to reveal a luminous circle that gradually grew in diameter until it took up almost a third of the sky. It was like a cut-out in the storm clouds which were threateningly tethered around it. A slightly pink-tinged white light was emanating from that area as it lit up the clouds and created grandiose effects of an overwhelming realism. Like in a sublime dream, I then saw a magical light coming down which covered us and the ground around us.

There were rays of light with dozens of astral entities rapidly approaching our group, entities whose diaphanous forms were the perfect embodiment of purity and beauty. The spectacle we were witnessing was even more extraordinary as all around us the forces of nature were unleashed and raging and created a very stark contrast. The entities seemed to ignore the storm. They too were emanating an intense light but of different colors and nuances than Machandi's.

Stunned, I was watching those entities with their human forms as they stopped in the air higher than Machandi and floated around us. Their smiling happy faces were radiating an unequalled happiness. I noticed that some of them had such bright faces that, instead of regular features, I could only see an oval of white light. Between their forms was a continuously perceivable play of multicolored lights that offered a special dynamism to the whole picture. Machandi, however, emanated the brightest light. Her magnificent brilliance radiated up to the open cave in the mountain and into much of the surroundings.

I heard her extra-special voice pierce my mind with great clarity. I looked at the goddess, but she was not moving her lips. It was a telepathic transmission, but it did not differ in any way from how I perceived her when I could hear her talking. In some respect, I could even say that the experience was now much stronger and more nuanced. I then intuitively knew that the goddess was simultaneously addressing the other nineteen people in the group in the same way and understood that each of us was receiving a message adapted to our own personality and specific individualities. Machandi offered us precious teachings about humanity and the way we need to act in order to be completely successful in our missions.

As far as I was concerned, her message was full of grace and delicacy, but I cannot reveal its content at this time which refers to some events I will be involved in during the near future. The effect of the éclat she was emanating was overwhelming and once more I felt I couldn't resist it due to the fact that my breathing was involuntarily stopping. I closed my eyes and abandoned myself completely. In that moment, the goddess looked beautiful beyond description as she came closer and closer to me. This time, I managed to cope with the brightness she irradiated, but I could not make any move.

Machandi came very close to me, just as she had in the sacred cave of Tibet. She placed her hand on the top of my head and kept it there. I felt shaken from the foundations of my being and slid into the void. I had no support or marks I could guide myself with. Everything around me seemed empty, save for the fact that emptiness was pulsating in an indefinite and mysterious way. The only thing I could do in that state was to contemplate the never-ending nothingness that surrounded me. Wherever I looked, I could see only an immense limitless void. That contemplation, in which I was completely immersed, was transcending any level of conceptual thinking. Even the intense thought of Machandi's presence had vanished, being integrated into the gigantic emptiness I was in. The words I am looking for now to describe that state seem insignificant. In the middle of that void emanating from me, I suddenly felt enveloped in an unequalled happiness that was continuously flowing, greater and greater, through my heart. Then, the horizon of my consciousness faded, but not before I felt like I had touched eternity.

When I came back and opened my eyes, I saw Elinor and Repa Sundhi not far away from me. They were whispering. I looked around, but there was no one else there. Machandi had vanished, the mountain wall was opaque once more, and the group of young people had left. On the horizon, I could see the dawn of a new day lighting a perfectly clear and pure sky. No trace of clouds, rain or wind was left. If the ground and stone were not wet, I could have sworn that there had been no storm a few hours before. Only the place that had been subtly protected by the yidam and where I had remained was dry and unaffected by the wrath I had witnessed not long ago. The air was cold but I could not feel it. I got up and approached Elinor and Repa Sundhi. I was walking slowly as if coming from another world.

"Machandi asked me not to disturb you from your meditative state," the lama said, addressing me. "In the meantime, the others left. You were still and profoundly absorbed for more than seven hours, but this very special experience you have lived through will have a great importance in your spiritual evolution."

I did not say anything. Everything seemed relatively remote and Repa Sundhi's words were barely piercing my mind. We unhurriedly gathered the few possessions we had brought there and then started to go down the mountain.

On the horizon, the red disc of the sun was gradually appearing and lighting our path back to the world...

THE END

EPILOGUE

My American editor suggested I write a short epilogue to the second volume in the series which ended quite suddenly. Without doubt, the way I ended the book was due to my psychic, mental and spiritual state that I felt after meeting with the goddess Machandi and the initiation received on the mountain. Many weeks passed in which I felt like I was floating in a reality situated on the edge of a dream and wakefulness, desiring with intensity to meet again with the goddess, but it did not happen.

Elinor left the country, and I remained in his elegant villa amongst the memories of his and Repa Sundhi's presence. After I calmed myself, I began to methodically analyze the amazing events I had experienced and the precious information I had received in the last few weeks. I deeply thought about these things and gradually started to meditate while surrounded by the peace and quietness of the superb villa. No matter how hard I tried to focus on these aspects, however, the luminous image of the goddess Machandi always appeared in front of my eyes, flooding my mind and inner experience with a happiness an ordinary man cannot easily understand.

The living universe of most people is relatively miniscule compared to the vastness of the subtle planes of manifestation and the great presence of the entities that exist there. Modern man lives, generally speaking, on the principles of fear and desire which are expressed in a very narrow sense, usually with reference to his immediate physical needs. There is therefore a huge disparity between his concept about the world and reality as it truly is.

I cannot really understand the "mechanism" of my destiny nor can I intuit the hidden nature of the plan which determines events from the recent period of my life. What I do know with a great certainty, however, is that they overwhelmed me with their intensity and revelation of some genuine realities. Looking back on that period of time with much detachment and understanding, I now realize the anxiety and exaltation of the soul I felt in my entire being. These then became the premise of some unexpected changes of situation and changes which radically modified the way of life I had lived up to that point. Nothing from all that has happened in the years that followed however was without the fundamental support of spirituality. My specific activities in the present imply such a thing too as these matters are at the limits of knowledge of modern science. It is a territory on the boundary of the unknown.

Finally, after a long period of time, I met with Repa Sundhi again, but this time he was accompanied by Shin Li, his charming assistant. This meeting also brought to a close my mission which had been outlined by the goddess Machandi: the translation and final editing of the secret parchment.

Many readers feel like they are being blessed when they read my books because they intuitively perceive, through the unknown spring of their hearts and souls, that the things I have exposed are true and come from an authentic source. Others, however, are filled with doubt, superficial thoughts, and by an inexplicable malice of disbelief regarding what is written here. Personally, I do not care if people believe or not what I write in my books because I know very well that the message arrives exactly where it is meant to.

The teachings I have received from Cezar, Dr. Xien and Elinor were really like true spiritual jewels that radically transformed my existence. They dovetailed extraordinarily with certain facts and events from the physical plane which were often unbelievable in their description. Readers insistently request "proof," either forgetting or not realizing that such an idea is quite comical in the present situation! First, they forget that my revelations do not at all represent a public "business" and that I am nothing other than a cog in an immense gear which through an extraordinary series of events has allowed me to publish these books. In volumes three and four, I have explained some of these aspects and circumstances. Even so, I see the need to reiterate that these books are only for those who have open hearts and minds.

Radu Cinamar
December 2010

PART II

By Peter Moon

1

RECOIL

If you are walking the earth and have just finished reading Radu's incredible tale, the chances are that you have been exposed to some startling new information which has challenged the way you think. Having said that, most of the information Radu relayed was not really new. It is quite ancient. What is new or novel, however, is his experience, particularly when you juxtapose it with modern humans. In other words, most modern humans are not privy to such information or exposed to similar experiences. Just as it was alluded to in the book, they are not particularly evolved nor are they inclined to be in synch with the information presented in this book. The whole idea of this book, however, is based upon the proposition that this will change.

Based upon the feedback I have received thus far, most readers have responded positively to Radu's book. There is also a minority who have issues. Some are not comfortable with the way Radu expresses himself. In *Transylvanian Sunrise*, Radu stated very clearly why he wrote the book the way he did. It was to tell the story as succinctly as possible and get the information out. He has done a great job, and I personally have no trouble understanding him. As far as Romanians go, Radu speaks very good English. I believe, however, that the reason some are uncomfortable with his writing is that it takes them out of their comfort zone. It challenges you to look at things in a way that you might not otherwise consider. Besides that, it is written from someone who comes from a different culture.

Many Americans are ethnocentric to the point where they are not really conscious of the living and breathing nature of other cultures. Although Radu speaks English well, some people do not really grasp that he is Romanian and although Romanians have had much exposure to American culture through media, they think, feel, act, and have cultural habits that are distinctly Romanian. I have done my best to bridge the gap with regard to idioms and phrases. It is beneficial to anyone reading this book to extrovert themselves beyond their ordinary horizons and realize that you are getting perspective from someone who is from a different culture and someone that you are very lucky to be hearing from at all. Also keep in mind that he is getting his focus from a Tibetan who is getting his focus from a member of the Blue Race. There is a plethora of different cultures and esoteric threads at work.

For those who either like the book or can surpass their judgmental tendencies, there is also the factor of emotional response. All of the books I have written or published are inclined to trigger significant or deep emotional responses in people. That is simply because the subject matter is interesting and meaningful in a way that other literature too often is not. Emotions are defined both as a mental state and also as feelings. They have everything to do with your motor functions in the brain and how you behave, act or respond. Keep in mind that the word *motion* is a part of the word *emotion*. This book triggers emotions because it is putting forth the prospect that you might be able to feel a whole lot better than you ever thought about feeling and just maybe there is a bigger answer to all of the little answers.

There are, of course, those who respond with enmity. Radu said that while many feel blessed to read his books, there are others who are "filled with doubt, superficial thoughts, and by an inexplicable malice of disbelief regarding what is written here."

It is one thing to dispute information, question it or doubt it. These are understandable responses. Malice or vindictiveness, however, is an entirely different matter. It is the intent to cause harm or injury. There is also a band of emotion which is not quite as harsh as malice and that is bitterness or resentment (expressed or unexpressed).

If anyone has questions or doubts about the material, that is routine and can be addressed. Those who have feelings of malice or bitterness towards Radu or his information, however, are not much different than the fanged sheep dogs he referred to in Chapter 4 that were trying to stop his meeting with Machandi. In other words, such people have something within their psyche that has become an agent of the forces which are opposed to the ideas presented in this book.

It is widely accepted that human beings are very limited in their comprehension of the universe and even the mysteries of how their own brain operates. When someone else comes from outside of their normal reference frame, however, and either presents the truth or even a model of the truth, it has a tendency to create a visceral reaction in homo sapiens. After all, Elinor presents ideas in his discourses that make the average man look like a clueless fool in the world scheme. What Repa Sundhi and Machandi reveal only add to this proposition. Although people know very well that they do not have the entire cosmos figured out, they can sure get upset when their systemized thinking about it is shown to have some gaping holes in it.

Radu's story suggests that we are at a point in world history where macrocosmic changes in consciousness will occur in the near future and critical thinking will be valued at a premium. In his book, he has presented ideas and discourse. There is no enforcement of the truth. It is only his story based upon his experiences and should be digested as such.

I will now address some of my impressions and experiences with regard to the circumstances surrounding this book, Radu, and my own personal adventures in Romania.

2

THE SACRED JOURNEY

As I have clearly alluded to already, there are strange reactions to Radu's work. Some are concerned that it is all a mind control operation or perhaps that I have become mind controlled in the process. This is almost very funny. What happens is that people read information that overwhelms their own thinking process, and they begin manifesting mind control behavior themselves. This is typical as most of the world has long been subject to mind influence if not outright mind control.

In actual fact, Radu's first manuscript sat in my office for some four years before I could complete reading it. Even though I enjoyed it, I was still suspicious with regard to whether it would be economically viable to publish it. Most people do not realize that the internet and other factors have reduced the publishing world to a fraction of what it used to be. In 1992, when I entered this business, there was a burgeoning industry with regard to metaphysical and occult books. Almost all of the companies from that time period are long gone. There is currently only one distributor left from that genre, and they are only a fraction of their former operation. I also have mainstream distribution channels but even they are reduced from the good old days. In any event, the main point here is that one has to be very careful when they publish anything. Even though Radu's book offers great entertainment value, there was no guarantee of instant cash or even that the book would generate significant interest. The merits of any given book do not always determine its success.

Once I got over the hurdle of actually publishing the book, I was eager to read the sequel. It actually took me years to acquire permission and a translation, so please understand that no one was forcing me or unduly influencing me. To be honest, getting the permission and translation was more akin to pulling teeth. I had written to my Romanian publisher to secure a deal but never heard back. Eventually, I received an email a year later telling me that my emails had ended up in the spam folder. It would take several months to work this out and it culminated with an in-person visit in Romania. While this meeting is not a part of the narrative you are about to read, it is significant to keep in mind that it happened in the context of other important events which embrace the cutting edge of technology on this planet.

Upon my initial reading of *Transylvanian Sunrise*, I began negotiating with the publisher to secure publishing rights in the English language. This took several months. As soon as we came to an agreement, I was contacted formally by Dr. David Anderson* of the former Time Travel Research Center for the first time in five years. He was inviting me to Romania. The timing of these two events was extraordinary and did not go unnoticed by me. As synchronicity is the hallmark of my writing career, I thought that the two events must be connected. I was particularly struck by the fact that when I had last met with David, he had said that he would not be able to work with me for another five years. It was now five years to the month and he had popped into my life again.

When I finally got to speak with David again, it was on the phone and we talked for an hour, mostly about scheduling and logistics for what would be my first trip to Romania. When I

* Dr. David Anderson is a mysterious scientist who has studied and discovered time control technologies that have real world applications. I have written about the history of this elsewhere, including the book *Transylvanian Sunrise* and in several issues of the *Montauk Pulse* newsletter which is issued quarterly by Sky Books and has been in publication since 1993. Dr. Anderson once owned the Time Travel Research Center located in an industrial park on Long Island. In the last few years, he has launched Anderson Multinational and the Anderson Institute which has reacquired and extrapolated upon the time control technologies once extant on Long Island. Key aspects of his technology are discussed in Appendix A and Appendix B of this book.

took the opportunity to ask him if he knew Radu Cinamar, David demurred and said we would speak about that when I got to Romania. He did acknowledge that he knew who I was talking about. When I asked if I could have a meeting with Radu, David seemed to think that would be possible and said he would have his people contact him. After such an encouraging response, I assumed that I would be learning many more mysteries about the hidden knowledge beneath the Romanian Sphinx as well as David's operations. There appeared to be some intriguing connections that would now be revealed. As those of you who have read *Transylvanian Sunrise* already know, this was not the case. I learned very little during my first visit to Romania.

Due to professional commitments with business associates, David had to remain silent for the time being. Other than telling me about what would be the future launching of Anderson Multinational, pretty much all he told me was that people had told him that he knows Radu. This tidbit of information was prompted by the fact that my Romanian publisher, Sorin Hurmuz, had visited me and delivered an audio CD from Radu that was specifically for me. At the end of the CD, however, Radu said to keep it silent but that I could share it with David Anderson who he would also like to meet. Apparently, Radu did not know David, but David seemed to think otherwise. This was a great mystery that would not solve for quite a while.

After *Transylvanian Sunrise* was finally published in the Spring of 2009, I returned to Romania in order to participate in the Atlantykron Conference which is sponsored by David's charitable organization called the World Genesis Foundation. This time, David was lecturing on time control technologies in a way that he never had before. He had me participate in his lectures and we dedicated one block of time to me talking about nothing else other than the events in *Transylvanian Sunrise*. While that book has sold many copies in Romania and has enjoyed a significant degree of popularity, most Romanians that I encountered had never read the book. Some had heard about it or the circumstances surrounding the events in the book but only one person I met had actually read it. Ironically, his name was Radu, but he was not Radu Cinamar.

Most of what David lectured on is now available on his website *www.andersoninstitute.com*. The most important point of what he had to say was regarding a concept in math which is known as the *invariance of the space-time interval*. This is a mathematical formula in conventional mathematics, but its implications are not well understood in scientific circles. If properly understood, it demonstrates that time is convertible to distance. If you read most definitions of the word *time*, they will clearly state that time is not defined in terms of space or distance. This ends up confusing the subject of time because it steers the way scientists have been taught. David tries to teach the value of looking at other points of view and thinking in ways that are outside of the box.

This particular year, David had plenty of time to answer my questions and graciously spent over an hour personally tutoring me on the invariance of the space-time interval. He was disappointed that most of the students did not seem to be grasping it but was happy that I did. In fact, he said that there were only about four physicists in the world at that time who really understood it. With David's blessings, I wrote an article for the Fall 2009 edition of the *Montauk Pulse* which makes it even simpler to understand. I have added it to this book as Appendix A if you are interested and are not intimated by the Pythagorean Theorem which is relatively easy to understand if you can grasp elementary geometry and algebra. The primary point is that once you can convert time to distance, all equations with regard to time can be converted into algebra. This is the entry point to understanding the mathematics behind time control technologies. This, in turn, leads to time travel itself.

At the end of the Atlantykron Conference, David told me that he would be making some big announcements towards the end of the year. He also said that he would visit me on Long Island in the next few months.

As soon as I finished at Atlantykron that same year, I was slated to go on another journey and this would be to the spiritual and cultural capital of ancient Transylvania: Sarmizegetusa. This is a carefully laid out assortment of stone and wood that goes back to the ancient Dacians who had bloody wars with the Romans around the First Century whereupon their culture was mostly wiped out. On my first trip to Atlantykron, I was advised by the professors and esoteric people that I should make it my business to visit the ancient capital.

I was very lucky to be accompanied by a lovely young girl, Nicole Vasilcovschi, who would act as my companion and tour guide. I had met Nicole the previous year shortly after I had arrived. She came up to me and gave me a big hug. This is not a typical Romanian greeting to a stranger, but Nicole told me that she recognized my spirit and saw that she would learn many things from me. As she was an important part of the journey, I will say a few things about her.

Nicole is a member of the Romanian Orthodox Church, and this affiliation has a lot to do with a dream she had when she was six years old. Jesus embraced her as light filled into her crown chakra as she spun around. After that experience, she could miraculously read the *Bible*. Not knowing exactly how to respond to Nicole's experience, her parents sent her to church where she has practiced the Orthodox faith ever since.

Nicole is an author who has written books on economics and has had several books of poetry published as well. As I write this, she is completing the last year of a PhD in International Business and Diplomacy. She speaks several languages and will probably become a career diplomat.

This year, before our trip to Transylvania, Nicole and I met with one of David's friends at Atlantykron who is psychic and very knowledgeable about esoteric matters. She prefers to remain nameless and does not speak English so Nicole translated for me. She told us that Romanian is a coded language and that it is the original language from which Latin was derived, not the other way around as is commonly thought by Westerners. This lady told us that we should expect to have profound experiences at Sarmizegetusa, but that it is best to spend three days there for a full experience. We were also told that it is the journey itself to Sarmizegetusa that is so important. It is literally a pilgrimage. Even so, I was no pilgrim in any conventional sense as I had no preconceived ideas or religious convictions.

The most exalted god of the ancient Dacians was Xalmoxis, a name which means "leaping god" because he is said to have transformed himself into a god from the human state. According to the Greek historian Herodotus, Xalmoxis was a disciple and servant of Pythagoras and transformed himself into a god after which he came back to his home country, the land which is now Transylvania, and created a spiritual tradition of which Sarmizegetusa was the capital. If you study a little deeper, you will discover that Xalmoxis, or at least another character of the same name, existed long before Pythagoras and that Sarmizegetusa is much older as well. Further, the *moxis* in Xalmoxis equates to the name *Moses*. It is also part of historical legend that Xalmoxis taught the Egyptians their ancient knowledge and literally spearheaded that ancient civilization. This vestigial remnant of history took on a little more meaning for me when I found out that the city of Sinaia, the first city I was taken to in Romania in 2008 and which is not too far from the Sphinx, means Sinai, the same locale where Moses experienced communion with his master. The more I have learned about the history, anthropology and archeology of Eastern Europe, the more apparent it is that key components of the Egyptian civilization originated from this area.

In any event, Nicole and I set out on our magical journey on the day we left Atlantykron. We were accompanied by Cristina Balin from Nicole's home town of Suceava which is in northern Romania. Like Nicole, Cristina is highly intelligent. She speaks even better English as she has spent significant time in the United States. She was studying to be a dentist at that time and should have her degree by now.

If the journey itself to Sarmizegetusa was the key component of the experience, we were confronted with this aspect right away. The first part of our journey required great patience. We had to wait some six hours for our initial train to depart. Once we did that, we had to change trains and seats on those trains frequently. Cristina and I got about two hours of sleep as we rode the train the entire night. Nicole stayed up the whole time.

At the outset of our trip, we attempted to offset the arduous journey by creating a film about it. Cristina was to be a spy from Department Zero who met us at the train station and asked if she could travel with us for safety reasons. This created some very interesting dynamics and story lines with Nicole acting stranger and stranger as we got to Transylvania. Most of the footage I took is unfortunately unusable as the sound of the train makes the audio challenging. In any event, it was fun.

It is important to stress the arduousness of the journey for any of you who might care to take it. I know there are people who follows the traces I leave in books and any adventurers should not take what I say lightly. In the wee hours of the morning, sometime after midnight, the train stopped in the middle of nowhere. There was a lot of chattering by the passengers in Romanian as to what we would do next. There was no conductor to tell you anything. Nicole heard from others that we would have to get off the train and catch another one down the railroad track.

I was standing near the edge of the exit and someone said to jump. There were no stairs but only a ladder that was not too encouraging as it did not extend very far down from the rail car which was over three feet from the ground. I jumped on to the rocks that surrounded the tracks below and wondered what in the hell was going on. The girls handed me all of our luggage and then I helped them down. Then everyone else got off of the train and down the precarious ladder. I am pretty tall so the jump was not too bad, but there were old ladies on that train. I had to be first for some reason. After we got off, everyone helped each other. That was the easy part. We then redistributed our luggage amongst ourselves so that we could each carry the proper weight for our size and ran over large rocky gravel to catch the next train. I, of course, had the most weight. It was a very long "run" as there was not time to walk leisurely. If the weight was too much to carry, the rocks underneath were equally uncomfortable.

After another train ride, we had to take a similar excursion and switch seats on the same train. On the last leg of our journey into Transylvania itself, we had to stand in the covered back of the car and outside of the main cabin as it was full. Finally, when we arrived in Transylvania, we arrived at an old and apparently deserted train station at about 4:00 a.m.. This was not encouraging. There were several other passengers and one of them said something. Nicole pointed to an empty and desolate looking train and said that it was our train. This was odd as there were no lights or sign of any other life. It was so much like the driverless carriage in the movie *Dracula* that I could not help but laugh. The seen was so odd and eerie that when I pointed this out to the girls, they laughed too.

We entered the dark train and waited in the mysterious quiet. Our exhaustion was tempered by the mystery of what we would experience next. A conductor came down the aisle and stood next to us. Nicole asked him a question, but he did not answer. He just stood like frozen robot. After a very non sequitur lag in his communication — at least fifteen seconds — he said we would leave soon. The emergency lights then came on as if he and the train had been activated by some mysterious force. The regular lights came on after that and we soon departed. None of this was actually mysterious force per se, but it is indicative of what one might experience on a quest to Sarmizegetusa. You are penetrating the unconscious aspects of your mental and spiritual network. The conductor played his part very well.

We arrived at our destination at sunrise at about 5:30 a.m. in the small village of Orastie and waited a little over a half hour for Father Antonius to pick us up. Father Antonius is a bishop of a monastery of the Old Orthodox Church. He was our host and was extremely thoughtful and courteous to our needs for our two night visit. He drove us to the monastery, showed us around and made sure we were fed.

Immediately taking us into his office, where he also slept, Father Antonius excitedly showed us pictures he had taken in Jerusalem. One was of a Madonna and baby Christ who were both black. I asked him why they were both black but go no answer. He then showed me a footprint on a rock from the Mount of Olives that is, according to legend, the last footprint of Jesus on Earth. I took a strong interest in this topic because Jesus is said to have ascended to heaven from the Mount of Olives. I have written a book, *The Montauk Book of the Living*, that is all about synchronicities with regard to the subject of olives.

During the writing of that book, I discovered that the olive is wrapped up into the deepest mysteries of many religious and oracular traditions, only one of which is Christianity. Those are explained in the book, but my own personal interaction with the theme of the olive proved to be equally intriguing and mysterious. It was my fleeting association with Olive Pharoah, the Matriarch of the Montauk Indians, which propelled me to revisit and rediscover salient events in my own life which were intertwined with the theme of the olive. My first out-of-the-body experiences took place on Olive Drive in Davis, California and in a location that was nearby olive trees. Second, my parents were killed in a crash and buried on the land that once was Rancho Los Olivas, the historical memory of which has been preserved by Los Olivas Adobe near Ventura, California. The focal point of Adobe Los Olivas is a fountain beneath an olive tree.[*] Third, there was a legendary blue Amazon queen of Atlantis named Antinea who gave Mankind the olive. Her name was transliterated by the Greeks into Athena. Through name associations and genetic heritage links, I could trace the ancestors on both sides of my parental family trees to Antinea's descendants: the Berbers of North Africa. More

---

[*] Egypt was known as the Land of the Olives in ancient times and Isis was known as the Queen or Lady of the Olives. Egyptians also used olive leaves to bury their dead as the olive was a symbol of the pathway to and from this world.

important to this book, the theme of a blue Amazon queen ties to Radu's encounter with Machandi. I have also written quite a bit about the Blue Race itself in both *The Montauk Book of the Living* and *The Black Sun: Montauk's Nazi-Tibetan Connection*. None of this seemingly relates too specifically to my journey to Transylvania save for the fact that Jesus is supposed to have ascended to heaven from the Mount of Olives. With all of these synchronicities connected to what might be considered the greatest event in the history of the Western Civilization, I was more than a little interested in the alleged footprint of Jesus being on the Mount of Olives.

The bishop told me that the actual footprint was one of a set of two original footprints, but that one was taken to Istanbul many years before. The footprint on the Mount of Olives resides within a mosque that is in the hands of the Muslim faith to this day. Nearby, there is another alleged spot on the Mount of Olives that also claims to be the spot where Jesus ascended from and was turned into a Russian Orthodox Church centuries ago. This church was used as a pretense by the British and French to start the Crimean War. They claimed they wanted the keys to the church which were in the hands of the Russians. In fact, it was just a humble clergyman who held the actual keys. This particular story is important to my quest, however, because the Crimean War actually created the country of Romania which did not exist as such before that war. If there had been no fight over the church on the Mount of Olives, there would be no country of Romania as such. The story of Cezar Brad, Radu Cinamar, and Doctor Xien would have played out entirely differently.

It is also very important to add that if it were not for my experiences that were highlighted by the mysterious theme of the olive, I would never have been in the circumstances I was in that would enable me to publish Radu's work and take this mysterious journey to Sarmizegetusa. The common denominator in my adventures was the Mount of Olives which symbolizes the end times in the *Bible*.

Although the bishop was enthusiastically showing us his other photos of Jerusalem, my interest waned after the Mount of Olives, mostly because I was exhausted on only a couple hours of sleep. Cristina, who had no more sleep than myself, was nudging me to stay awake out of respect to the bishop. I soon fell completely asleep. When I eventually woke, I looked up and everyone was laughing. It was now recognized that it was time for us to go to bed. After resting for a few hours, we had lunch in the dining hall and it was time now for a much more animated discussion.

As we ate, Father Antonius talked at length to the girls who are both of the New Orthodox faith. He only speaks minimal English so they translated for me. The dialogue was quite interesting as he began explaining the "war in the heavens" between demons and angels and the cosmic struggle that occurs on Earth between the forces of good and evil. I do not mean to suggest that he is wrong, but he takes it quite seriously and speaks about it in a candid reference frame, somewhat akin to Bob Costas or Al Michaels of NBC talking about the NFL playoff forecast for the Super Bowl.

When he asked about myself and my vocation, I referenced the war between angels and demons and related that to the electronic manipulation that occurred in the Montauk Project. Much of the Montauk Project dealt with different domains. At the top you had heaven and at the bottom you had hell. Electronic frequencies were matched to each domain and equipment was created that either emulated those domains or influenced them. In other words, I told him that the demon realm used electronics to do their dirty work. I also gave him a very quick summary of my work with Dr. David Anderson and his breakthroughs with regard to time control technology.

I should also mention at this point that Father Antonius is not only the bishop or abbot of this monastery, but he is also an exorcist. He takes his mission quite seriously. The Old Orthodox Church is much smaller than the New Orthodox Church. The former believes in helping the poor and sick while the latter is far more inundated with modern commercialism and political controversy. The Old Orthodox Church strives to be pure and is generally considered to be beyond reproach.

I never thought about it until I got home, but the odds of someone going to Transylvania and being hosted by an exorcist are obviously quite rare. Further, if you are going to go on a sacred journey, having an exorcist in the mix makes for great drama. I certainly did not intend it that way. I would have preferred to stay in a hotel, but Nicole saw to all of the arrangements and she was trying to avoid me having to spend money which was not something I asked her to do. Father Antonius was evidently meant to be a part of our remarkable journey to Sarmizegetusa.

After lunch, Father Antonius drove us to two major cities of Transylvania, Hunedoara and Deva, and took us sight-seeing. During our meal, Father Antonius had said that at least eighty percent of the people are under the influence of the devil who gets to many of them through their habit of smoking. Maybe some sixteen percent are relatively free to exercise their free will. Later in the afternoon, as he drove us through the streets, I pointed to someone who was smoking and said, "The Devil!" He liked that and laughed. Not long afterwards, he asked me if there was anything he could do for me during my stay. I told him yes and asked him to pray that we would have a successful journey to Sarmizegetusa the next day.

Later that evening, I experienced a remarkable synchronicity that is mysteriously tied to the events I have earlier described with regard to the olive theme. As Nicole and I stood outside the monastery in the evening, we were speaking with one of the monks who mentioned that the first stone of the monastery was placed on August 11, 1999, the day of a full solar eclipse. Tomorrow would be August 11th and the tenth anniversary of that date. What was remarkable to me was that August 11, 1999 was the exact day I met Dr. David Anderson. He was the one responsible for me coming to Romania in the first place.

The period from August 10th to August 14th is significant because it is recognized as a major biorhythm of the Earth's energy grid. The August 12th date gets most of the credit because that date is believed to be when the actual Philadelphia Experiment of 1943 occurred as well as the climax of the Montauk Project in 1983. August 12th is also referred to as the birthday of the Egyptian goddess Isis (Queen of the Olives). It is a time when the star Sirius is at its closest point to the Earth and is sacred to the ancient Egyptians who recognized Sirius as the home of their ancestors as do the Dogon of Africa who learned this from and were culturally interconnected with the Amazigh Berbers of the Sahara. On August 14th, 2003, there was a major blackout in the northeastern United States, the epicenter of which was Preston Nichols' new home in Cairo, New York. All of these time associations are interesting because it was also August of 2003 when the amazing discoveries were made beneath the Romanian Sphinx that are discussed in *Transylvanian Sunrise*.

The most notable aspect of the above mentioned series of synchronicities had to do with the fact that we were taking our sacred journey to Sarmizegetusa the next day, August 11, 2009. At this time, Nicole also informed me that David Anderson had left a nice message on her cell phone saying that he wished he could be with us. He had been invited to make the trip but his business responsibilities prevented this.

Father Antonius had us woken up at 5:30 a.m. the next morning and saw that we had breakfast. At 6:30 a.m., we got into a taxi that he had arranged to take us on the ride to Sarmizegetusa which would take a little less than an hour. The roads to this locale are not on the main highways and it was a very bumpy ride, the last part being a dirt road. As we climbed up the mountain at one point, the car stalled inexplicably. Whether it was or not, and I would say that it was, it seemed like a spiritual force making itself known. It was kind of obvious. Once this was recognized, the car regained power and we made the final ascent. We arrived about 7:30 a.m. and made our way down the short trail. There are signs warning you to be careful as there are poisonous vipers nearby. Until noon, we had the whole area completely to ourselves. We explored the various formations and did lots of filming. Ideally, one is supposed to spend three days in Sarmizegetusa whereby it will have a profound effect on you. This would require camping just outside the park in a tent. The park itself has a spigot of running water, but there are no bathrooms.

Unfortunately, we did not have time to explore Sarmizegetusa to the extent we would have liked. The focal point of most visitors is on the solar wheel and the surrounding temple ruins. There is also a square pit made of stones that is out of sight and behind the solar wheel that was probably once used as a water receptacle. There has also been speculation that it was used for human sacrifice at some point. There are stories of people being sacrificed to Xalmoxis, but I do not know if they are true. If so, they might be a degenerative form of the original teachings. For me, my journey to Sarmizegetusa was not even a superficial archeological study. I was going for the experience. We explored and also concentrated on the filming. I got several good shots and put these together in a video that included a summary of my first visits to Romania.

Perhaps the most interesting thing that happened at the park itself was after we had made our initial explorations. It was about noon, and we were eating the lunch we had brought with us. I then noticed two people standing still in the middle of the solar wheel. They looked like they were doing chi gong, an ancient oriental practice which means "breath work" and is something that I do every day. I went over by myself to investigate and saw a woman there alone. She spoke English very sparingly, but I was able to get across to her that I was publishing Radu Cinamar's works in America. When I told her this, she had a strong emotional reaction and started crying. Her name is Lenutz. A man then arrived who was her husband and we all engaged in a very friendly but rather abstract conversation as there was a language barrier. I brought them over to Cristina and Nicole where we enjoyed rapid translation. The couple said they were doing energy work and that they visit different sacred sites in Romania from

SOLAR WHEEL — SARMIZEGETUSA

time to time. They eventually gave me a magazine that explains the very unique mathematical formula that the solar calendar is based upon. I cannot read the magazine at this point as it is in the Romanian language. If I were to be sarcastic, I would say that the math was based upon "base 1.5." It was obtuse to me.

Lenutz and her husband took us on a mountain hike to see a sentinel post. They also explained that the entire region of Sarmizegetusa went for miles around, but people mostly just think of it only as the area around the solar wheel. When we finished our extensive hike, they drove us back to Orastie. We all agreed that we would return to Sarmizegetusa the next year and every year thereafter. I wanted to take everyone out to dinner to show my appreciation for the enlightening day and all of the information and courtesy everyone had extended to me. Besides, Nicole had taken every precaution on her own initiative to make sure I would spend almost no money. That was not my idea, but I wanted to say thank you. Lenutz and her husband had to go somewhere so

M A P   O F   S A R M I Z E G E T U S A   C O M P L E X

T E M P L E   R U I N S   —   S A R M I Z E G E T U S A

WATER WELL — SARMIZEGETUSA

SUN DIAL — SARMIZEGETUSA

NICOLE

CRISTINA

OLD ORTHODOX MONASTERY

HUNEDOARA CASTLE

they could not join us. Nicole said there were no restaurants but maybe we could find a pizza parlor or something.

As I heard the girls talking in Romanian, I could tell that we were headed back on a long walk to the monastery. We were not going to a restaurant or pizza parlor of any kind because there were none. This is Romania. It was disappointing to me and not just because I wanted to show my appreciation. I was hungry and had been eating at the monastery or Atlantykron for a week. My long journey was almost over. I felt like sitting down at a restaurant and relaxing a bit. As we were all hungry, Cristina pointed to a rock on the corner of two streets. We sat on the grass and used the rock as a table to eat a meal of hard-boiled eggs, white bread, and tomatoes. This was a bit of culture shock. The girls, who do not come from poor families, took this in stride as such an instance is not so uncommon in Romania. They have also negotiated there way through colleges of higher learning on scholarships but are very savvy when it comes to budgeting, scraping by and cutting corners. It was a distinctly Romanian experience. On the way back, we saw a tree with small yellow plums and those became our dessert.

It then struck me that I would be in for a long train ride the next day with virtually no food. In order to avoid the chaotic change of trains that we had experienced on our trip to Transylvania, Nicole was planning to get me on a train where I would not have to change seats once. This was a relief, but the trade-off was that there would be no stops to eat nor would I even have a chance to go to a real grocery store. With regard to groceries, the girls were both in the same boat as they would be travelling the next day in the opposite direction but only for six hours. I had to travel nine hours to Bucharest.

Walking down the last few blocks before we would arrive at the country road to take the long walk to the monastery, we saw a small sign that said "kiosk" that was really a lower harmonic vestige of a 7-11 store. Someone was selling potato chips and the like out of a garage. This was apparently my last chance to get something to eat for tomorrow's trip, but there was absolutely nothing there that I would eat save for a bag of popcorn that Nicole insisted on paying for.

As we passed the very last house before the long road back to the monastery, a man came out of his house and pointed to the skies and said the Pleiades would be out tonight. He wanted to see them but the clouds were going to make it difficult. As he spoke only Romanian, Nicole translated. When I told him how lucky he was to live in such a beautiful environment, he became even more friendly and invited us to his home and organic garden. He started feeding us all sorts of vegetables and fruits and then started bringing out cakes and wine. By the time we were done, we had been fed up to our ears. Once again, an experience that was distinctly Romanian. He also provided us with bags of food for the train ride the next day. I had a bag of pears, apples and oranges which made the return trip much more pleasurable. Perhaps the prayers of the bishop had been answered. This man regularly provides food for the monastery. It capped off a very successful journey.

Although our physical journey was essentially done, the sacred aspect was not finished by a long shot. Both evenings I was at the monastery, I committed myself to a specific chi gong exercise every night for one hour. I eventually continued this exercise for thirteen months. If any professional boxer would do this particular exercise for a year, he would never be in danger of punching himself out. In fact, he could punch continuously for the entire fight provided he did not get himself knocked out. Besides that, it has tremendous health and spiritual benefits. Before I would go to bed each night, and even though I was very tired, I would go out on the balcony of the monastery and do this exercise for one hour into the Transylvanian night. In the far distance, I could see an explosion of light reaching up into the night sky. Nicole explained to me that the New Orthodox Cathedrals, which are very ornate, are built with open spaces at the top that are shaped like crosses and they light up the night sky. It was a poetic scene.

In the early hours of August 12th, there was a surprise continuation of my sacred journey that would occur in my sleep. I had a very magical dream where I knew I was completely outside of my body. There was a bright blue sky and I could look over the entirety of Romania. Suddenly, I saw obnoxious black helicopters approaching a tall edifice which represented the central government or a similarly related institution. There was a huge dark cloud over this building that clearly represented a very dark cloud over Romania. These were not my conclusions, but it is simply how the information was presented to me in the dream. It was extremely dramatic and spoke of the truth. At least that was the context I was given. While experiencing the great freedom of an out-of-body experience, I was suddenly confronted with the opposite: mind control operations and worse in the archetypal form of a black helicopter. In the same vein, a flash of truth went through my mind that told me I was not connected to this dark cloud in any way. In other words, there was no danger. The cloud, however, was still a part of the landscape.

This dream obviously represents the lid that has been held down on the operations Radu Cinamar has written about in his books. He has mentioned the negative forces quite clearly. The black helicopter theme has another odd association with me in Romania. Whenever I go to Atlantykron, the director of the camp always mentions the status of the black helicopters that buzz the camp annually. David mentions it as well. It is as if I am viewed either as an expert or a receptacle for knowledge of such things. In actual fact, the only thing I know about black helicopters is what Preston Nichols has told me. He said that most of them are just regular army helicopters. The only ones with extra-sensory psychology equipment on them are from New Haven, Connecticut. They are equipped with spectrum analyzers that can zone in on the electromagnetic signature of an individual and also feature equipment that can transmit certain frequencies. The implications of this are as broad as your imagination. This data is dated from the mid 1990s.

I can say, however, that during my own investigation of Montauk, black helicopters would appear at suspicious times. For example, I might be thinking a certain type of thought with regard to mind control or penetrating various levels of secrecy within the Government and a black helicopter would appear suddenly and inexplicably. Whether they were transmitting the thought that I was thinking or whether they were in response to it is an open question. The general feeling I got, however, was that they were letting me know they were there in some capacity.

This latter feeling was corroborated when Tantra Bensko told me of her somewhat similar experiences. When she would be teaching tantric yoga in her living room, a black helicopter would appear, even to the point where the pilot would fly close enough to the ground in order to make eye contact with her. One night I had a similar experience, but it was in a dream. I watched the helicopter from my living room and saw the face of the pilot. He was an older man and really quite lame in power. After that, the black helicopter phenomena disappeared from my life.

My most interesting black helicopter experience occurred with my daughter who was very young at the time. We saw a helicopter in the backyard, hovering very low. As it banked and changed direction, I got into my car to follow it, but it disappeared in a way that defied logic. As soon as it left my view, the very loud noise it made ceased and the craft could no longer be seen. It really made me wonder if they had perfected the invisibility technology from the Philadelphia Experiment.

The fact that black helicopters were a theme in my dream suggests they are tied to the REM state of deep sleep. In my out of body experience, I was seeing astral phenomena that was interpreting itself through my brain as a black helicopter. No danger was indicated.

When I woke up for my last morning in Transylvania, I was doing my chi gong workout when I heard a knock at the door. It was Nicole. She had brought me a piece of Eucharist bread that had just been prepared in a ceremony that she had attended in the chapel below. It was not like a Catholic wafer but was a real piece of bread. Nicole wanted to know if I had eaten yet because it has to be taken on an empty stomach. As I had eaten a plum, she said I should wait until the next morning and take it then. She was very intent on me doing so.

Keep in mind that I am not a Christian and never have been. My friends from childhood even remember me being quite critical of this human institution and suggesting it was perhaps the most knuckle-headed thing invented by Mankind. It was not until I became an ordained minister for the Church of Scientology that I actually learned to respect and correlate all religious traditions. This was further enhanced by reading *777 and Other Qabalistic Writings of Aleister Crowley* which demonstrates how all religions correlate with the Tree of Life.

Most people who believe in Christianity have not fully examined their own gray matter that propagates their feelings or intellectual capacity with regard to how they are interpreting the data they are receiving about the subject. By gray matter I am referring to their own mental mechanisms which would also extend to their emotional and spiritual mechanisms. On top of that, virtually all Christians are completely ignorant of the name of their founder and what it represents in terms of ancient magic from millennia ago. Their understanding is often embarrassingly simplistic as if suitable for a school play. Christians, nevertheless, are no less spiritual than anyone else. Just like anyone else, they have their own filter between the divine and the physical world.

In Nicole's case, she is a very pure spirit and Christianity just happens to be her interface with the divine. Just as I had respected Father Antonius and asked for his prayers (which seemed to work), I told her that I would take the Eucharist the next morning out of respect to her. I also adore her.

Nicole and Cristina accompanied me to the train station where Nicole made double sure I would be on the same train and in the same seat all the way to Bucharest where I would be met by her friend Ana. We said goodbye, and I took the long nine hour train ride to Bucharest. The carrots, pears and other fruit that had been given to me came in very handy. The highlight of the trip, however, was the popcorn that Nicole bought for me. It hit the spot at the right time.

The train arrived in Bucharest at 9:00 p.m. and Ana was waiting for me right on time. A very friendly girl, Ana took me to a youth hostel which was a short walk away. Again, I would have preferred to have stayed in a hotel but everything had been arranged already. To go against the flow would have been cumbersome to say the least. I would spend the night in a large coed dorm with college age people. It made me feel young.

I took the Eucharist the next morning on an empty stomach and prayed for a miracle. That was the whole idea. Ana picked me up and showed me around Bucharest a bit before taking me to the airport. It was on the plane that the miracle occurred. After taking my seat, I saw one black man get on the plane. I made an immediate decision or prayer that this man would sit down next to me. As I am interested in and have written about the Moors of ancient history, I wanted him to sit by me in order that I might ask him about any sort of black community in Bucharest as there are hardly any blacks in Romania. His seat was right next to me.

As it turned out, this man was a Christian minister who was accompanied by a white woman from another church. They had been in Moldova in order to address and correct the abuse of a young boy who had been stoned at the instigation of a priest of the New Orthodox Church. The young boy was an orphan who had been adopted by a Pentecostal missionary and his wife. The minister had purchased a tractor for the local community but was perceived as a threat by the priest. He was not only a different domination of Christianity, he was helping the locals and would therefore gain credibility and popularity. The priest stirred up his congregation against the family and the young orphan was stoned and hospitalized in what became an international incident. This man and woman had been there to ensure that the boy got proper treatment and that the situation was calmed down and addressed as much as possible by the local authorities.

For me, I had honored Nicole's request and accepted her version of the Holy Spirit. What happened, however, was a ricochet effect. The Holy Spirit moved right through me, so to speak, and relayed back to her the contradictions in her own church. Nicole is a member of the New Orthodox Church. As Father Antonius prepared the Eucharist, we can credit him. Once again, he is from the Old Orthodox Church and does not engage in such contradictory behavior. I wrote about the experience in the *Montauk Pulse* and sent it to Nicole. I thought she might be a little sensitive to what I had written, but she enthusiastically congratulated me on the article and told me to put her last name in the article as well.

This was the end of my trip to Sarmizegetusa and Romania. At the urging of my most knowledgeable and educated Romanian friends, I had taken the sacred journey and touched the heart of ancient Transylvania. Although the physical travel was over, the sacred journey would continue in a most mysterious way that I would never expect and was centered around my association with David Anderson who I was scheduled to meet with upon my return to America.

3

NEW YORK

The year prior to my visit to Sarmizegetusa in 2009, I had received a fair amount of correspondence from Radu. He had repeatedly mentioned that he would like to meet me in person at some point. Shortly after returning to my home in New York after a vacation in California, I received an email from Radu telling me that he had come very close to my house on Long Island. He did not visit me, however, as he decided that it might cause me many potential problems if he did. It was as if those astral sheep dogs mentioned in his tale were following him. In light of things that have happened since, it might be a good thing. There is a lot of attention devoted to keeping his story subdued. Radu also stated that he missed Cezar (who had left) very much and said that things were very busy in Department Zero and that he might not be able to communicate for a long time. I did not hear from him again for pretty much an entire year.

After Radu's last letter, however, David Anderson became relatively available again and was buzzing with all sorts of information. This began with his presentation of the invariance of the space-time interval which I have discussed. His lectures at Atlantykron were very rich and intriguing. He followed that up with a visit to me at my house in October of 2009.

David was very interested in seeing the video footage I had taken at Atlantykron the previous two years. I showed him the Sphinx, Sarmizegetusa and a lot of different footage of Romania and Atlantykron. As we watched with a couple of friends, I realized that it was time to finally play the CD for him that Radu had given to me over a year earlier. I had sent a copy to David, but the pile of mail it found its way to was never opened.

As we listened to the CD, David maintained a conversation with one of my friends. It made me think he was not too interested, and I asked him if I should turn it off. No, he said. He was listening to everything and was interested. It seems that David can multi-task somewhat akin to a computer.

After he finished listening to the CD, his primary comment was that he was impressed at how much Radu had trusted me in telling me what he did. I will reiterate, however, that most of what Radu said is a confirmation of what is in *Transylvanian Sunrise*. It concerns details surrounding the events in *Transylvanian Sunrise* with a sincere apology that he cannot provide further proof. This, he said, is forbidden by his superiors and would result in him being cut off from the current access he has to such matters. In his message, Radu stated that he hoped to meet me fairly soon in the United States and also that he would like to meet David Anderson.

My next step was to ask David about the people who told him that he had met Radu. Before I could ask the question, David explained without me having to ask. He said that when I initially inquired about seeing Radu on my first trip to Romania (I had also asked to visit the Projection Hall in this same request), he initiated correspondence to effect such a meeting. I knew David was using his own office, but I did not know what channels he had at his fingertips to accomplish such. The entire correspondence initiated by his office ended up being forwarded through my publisher, the only public contact for Radu. I soon received an email from Radu stating that he could not meet me in Romania but that he hoped to meet me in the United States.

As it turned out, David said he had also personally contacted some of his friends in the Romanian government on my behalf. One of these people informed David that he had actually shaken hands with Radu, but nothing could be done at this time about getting me a visit. The fact that David was told this was based upon a long history of trust, respect and cooperation between him and his friend in the government. It apparently started with my request to meet Radu the previous year.

While this seems to resolve one step of the mystery, it presents yet another riddle. Before I asked David if I could meet Radu, I had asked him if he knew Radu. At first, he was not sure who I was talking about. Then, after I explained the contents of the book quickly to him, he said "Oh, I know who you mean. I'd prefer not to talk about that on the phone." He then went into a fairly long comment on how phone conversations are not secure in America and that he would be much more comfortable talking about this in Romania. I found this ironic because Radu felt more comfortable talking in America.

All of this communication leads to obvious bafflement. If David has shaken hands with Radu then why did Radu state that he would like to meet David, that he trusted him and that he wanted him to listen to the CD? As David and Radu are both involved in very mysterious operations, it was hard for me to fathom that there might be no connection between them. If there was, neither seemed to be aware of it.

Before he left, David said that he would be releasing a paper on time reactors in a couple of months and that I could include that in my *Montauk Pulse* newsletter. Even though David did not have all of the answers I wanted, what he eventually released about time reactors is nothing short of remarkable. It is covered in Appendix B of this book.

David followed up his release of information on time reactors by appearing on OtherWorldRadio with me on December 30th, 2009. This was his first radio appearance in over five years. When I had the chance to ask him a question, I asked him what I thought was a very interesting question: "In all of your research, what is the most humorous thing you've encountered?"

This is an off-the-wall sort of question, and I asked it because it represents the human factor which is very important to any sort of endeavor of this nature. There was no doubt as to his answer and he gave it without hesitation or thinking. He replied that it had to do with people's reactions when they actually witnessed the time chamber for the first time. He said they would almost always burst into laughter, presumably as a reaction to seeing their view of reality being suspended. In other words, reality is not quite the way they thought it was.

While David revealed quite a bit in his initial return to radio, he gave a much more dramatic presentation a month later when he publicly announced for the first time that human beings have been subjected to the controlled time reactor fields (see Appendix B for more information on the technology). This is a startling announcement because in all of his previous research, pretty much only plants, clocks and other objects had been used. Incredible progress has been made in the third generation of this technology where they achieved stability of the boundary layer as well as a significant increase in the size of the time-warp field. It is now deemed safe enough for human experimentation.

The time warp field or time chamber is created by means of stimulating a chemical reagent with high energy lasers and also utilizing a rotating electromagnetic field. As David describes it, the foundation of their patents is that they have actually created a path through hyperspace. The phenomena at work here is consistent with what is known in physics as a CTC or closed time-like curve. The key to understanding a closed time-like curve is that it is just time looping back on itself.[*]

A closed time-like curve was first proposed in modern physics by scientist Kurt Godel in 1949 who said that pathways in time are possible by using CTCs. His theory shows how heavy gravity can curve space-time in a way that allows time to loop back on itself. Godel's work was the first to suggest that going

---

[*] This was a key feature of the theories and adventures suggested by Preston in the Montauk scenario. If you want to get some idea of how this could play out in experience, I recommend a movie entitled *Time Travelers* from 1964. It is a campy but watchable story that demonstrates how a science project team jumps into a vortex they created and then go through all sorts of adventures only to end up at the same point where they jumped into the vortex. It was distributed as a video by Thorn EMI.

back into time could be possible without violating the laws of math and physics. Dr. Anderson has added more to Kort Godel's original outlook because his device not only retards the flow of time but also accelerates it. This means that his loops connect to the future and not just the past.

David was careful to state that this is really time control and not time travel. People have been exposed to accelerated and retarded rates of time. Where the line is drawn between "time control" and "time travel" I cannot really say but it seems to be a fine one.

He also stated that humans exposed to the time chamber can actually walk outside of the field and then interact with the time they were now in. He also stated that the technology is not far away from sending someone 40 to 50 years into the past. In short, David revealed that humans have been sent into the past but quickly stated that the Anderson Institute is surely not the only one to do this. Many governments, in conjunction with private industry, have been experimenting with time control technology for years.

Most spectacular is the excitement or start up of the time warp field. Tremendous and amazing experiences have been reported by the people being exposed to these fields. Some have very spiritual experiences and some report seeing spectacular phenomena as they experience the transition period of acceleration/deceleration. With regard to this type of information, David said that the human mind behaves very unusually when exposed to something so foreign. It is not consistent from person to person and this field of endeavor is not the particular expertise of the Anderson Institute at this time although they are trying to become more competent in that area.

Perhaps more important is that the nature of our reality is now subject to an unnatural state of change. The web of interdependence is so complex that it is beyond our capacity to predict the impact that this new time control technology will have. It is so powerful that it has the potential to literally erase history.

The great questions of history can soon be answered and any historical event will soon be subject to study and review. David has stated that we are way past the "what if" stage and "How do we use this technology?" is the question now.

The implications for society are huge, but there is a device that has been developed by the Anderson Institute that has the potential to act as a safeguard for unwarranted use of this technology and it is known as a Time Tremor Detector or TTD. If someone is experimenting with time, these TTDs will pick it up and indicate where the experiments are taking place. It is through the use of such devices that the Anderson Institute has become part of a web of research groups across the planet which includes but is not limited to India, China, South Korea, Russia, and Japan.

India is by far the most advanced and active of these countries pursuing time control technology. Their Ministry of Science and Technology in New Delhi has a Department of Research and Development Organization (DRDO) which has set up a time research project with a massive facility that is ten times larger in scale than anything anyone else has done. It is located in the Dighi Hills which is in the Pune District of the state of Maharashtra. Pune is an industrial hub fifty-eight miles from Mumbai (formerly Bombay) and there is a six lane highway connecting the two cities.

Time research, David stated, is one of the most competitive technologies in the world today and governments are trying to utilize it for their own self interest. It is therefore important that it be regulated and transparent. The Time Tremor Detector serves this purpose.

The scientific community is split down the middle as to whether time control technology should be disclosed or not. David is the leading proponent for disclosure and was planning to release a series of videos, but this has not happened as of yet.

On March 2nd, 2010 I had an opportunity to ask David Anderson some follow up questions on Sovereign Mind Radio, hosted by Sonia Barrett. One of the first questions I asked was if we would get to see some video of this new time control technology in the upcoming videos he was planning to release. He reminded me that the Discovery Channel had taken an entire film crew into his old facility on Long Island but the footage was restricted from publication. Film crews have also visited his new center in New Mexico and while he is hopeful it will be included in the upcoming videos, that depends upon approval from his partners.

I also referred to the accounts of the Montauk Project whereby video cameras had been sent back in time so as to view events in the past and future. Have they attempted anything similar at his research center? Can we look into the past?

With regard to remote cameras, scientists understand that any movement through time (accelerating and decelerating matter or information backward or forward in time), has an impact upon the construct of reality. Some feel, however, and David does not agree, that you can limit the effect this will have on the time line by sending cameras into time instead of living organisms. Unfortunately, there is a complex web of interdependencies that make up the nature of our reality and by changing one small element, it might create more than just a small ripple.

India, he said, is sending camera-equipped drones into a time-warp field. There is, however, a problem with visible light being able to propagate through the boundary layers of the time warp field. The Anderson Institute is trying to work out a solution, but the best results thus far obtained are by sending a camera into the past and then getting it back out.

The whole idea of sending drones into the past is quite amusing because such a device would be looked at as a UFO if it was sent back to the Fifties or most any other decade. This makes one wonder what role time research from the future has played in the UFO phenomenon of recent times. When we consider that it is India sending drones into the past, it is even more bizarre because the media in India has long reported on a sporadic phenomena known as the "Monkey Man," a small creature either made with or amalgamated with metal that bites or ravages people with its metal claws and sounds like a bizarre science experiment. That it was witnessed in New Delhi is ironic because that is where the time experiments in India more or less originated.

Sonia asked David if he had ever looked into the Philadelphia Experiment and Montauk Project. With regard to the P.E., he said there is a trail of correspondence revealing major scientists were involved in this and certainly more than official sources will declare. As for Montauk, there are too many pieces that do not fit with regard to the official story. He said it is quite clear that the publicly stated use of that facility is not accurate. There are still many questions that need to be answered. I suggested that when the capabilities of the time chamber are up to it that these two incidents can be focused on, at least to try to figure out what happened. He thought that was an interesting idea.

The UFO factor, just alluded to in the aforementioned comment about India, comes into play here because, according to different sources, flying saucers came in by the bucket load when a rift of space-time was created during the Philadelphia Experiment. While this is the stuff of legend, it correlates with what David has told us about closed time-like curves. Maybe the story of saucers is really true and they were responding to a TTD.

This scenario with UFOs also correlates with what David has said about various governments being on the verge of time wars or controlling time to their own advantage, possibly at the expense of the population. Preston had always heard from secret government circles that World War II was a war of time and that the Nazis had originally won. In any case, this new technology from the Anderson Institute causes us to revisit these ideas with a fresh vigor. It gives us reasons to wonder about many things.

This idea of focusing the time chamber on key events is a fascinating one because one could also apply it to the censorship that time research and other sensitive matters have been subjected to. I mention this because David explained that censorship is a fundamental strategy of how corporations and governments succeed and prosper. Censorship of consciousness is key. The Anderson Institute is trying to get people to look beyond the unconscious censorship of their own human senses that their cultural and biological evolution has imposed upon their ability to see things. Individuals need to expand their capacity in this regard, but the whole idea of viewing the history of censorship itself is a fascinating one. He liked that idea, too.

All of this, however, tells you how powerful this technology is if it can do what he says, and there is every indication to believe him. It is clear this technology can potentially solve all the world's major problems. Implementing it is an entirely different matter and that is probably THE major problem. The resistance can already be anticipated, but the idea of turning the device on key problems makes it unstoppable. Just think about it. All of this is why David is so keen on establishing a public moral compass that serves everyone. Time control technology is powerful beyond anyone's imagination. If history proves to be an experiment in time, as he has suggested, perhaps we will soon be able to view it.

As interesting as all of these musings are, I am even more intrigued by the prospect of how David's research correlates with the adventures of Radu Cinamar and why I have been placed in the midst of these two remarkable scenarios. While David was coming out with all of this information, however, Radu had been silent for a very long time. It made me think that whenever one of them heats up, the other one will cool down. When I was getting lots of correspondence from Radu, David was mostly silent or non-responsive. Now it was the other way around.

4

MONTAUK

After the radio show with Sonia Barrett, I had a dream where I was waiting in a hotel for David Anderson. One person in the dream said he worked with David, and I will refer to him as Solomon. I then saw myself at a table in the hotel having breakfast with David and one other person.

When I consulted a dream dictionary, it indicated a table refers to a meaningful discussion with someone or something you can count on. I received an email from David right after this dream asking if we could have a face to face meeting soon. He did not say why he wanted to meet with me.

As I was helping to prepare a seminar at Montauk courtesy of Sacred Spirit Tours (which was to celebrate the return of the Montauk Medicine Man, Artie Crippen, to Montauk), I asked David if he would like to come and visit me there. He responded that he would like to come but also wanted to know if it would be all right if he did a presentation. I was delighted, particularly when he said that he wanted to show a video of his time chamber. David said the videos he wanted to do were held up as he had not been able to get clearance on showing the time chamber in the videos, but there was nothing forbidding him to show it to a small number of people. Although advertising that David would attend and do a presentation at the Montauk event would have increased the attendance considerably, I suggested that we keep it secret as it could have attracted a lot of attention we did not want. David like this idea, too.

The seminar was held at Montauk from April 9-11. The impetus for all of this began at a Sweat Lodge on Super Bowl Sunday in 2009 which was instigated by my Chi Gong teacher, Roosevelt Gainey, who had said to Artie that he wanted to do a Native American sweat lodge. When I found out about this, I suggested my friend Vicky Lagoudis (*www.teachingspirit.com*) who has a sweat facility. Besides the aforementioned, it was attended by myself, Sandra Sabatini, Shaman Sharon Jackson (also known as Winona Red Bird, Queen of the Montauks) and a few other unnamed participants.

The sweat lodge included four rounds of intense heat focusing on cleansing, purification, healing, and the spirit world. Natives used the sweat lodge before a hunt, war, healing an illness, and virtually any important activity in their lives. It is a potent way to address and integrate all issues related to the body, mind and soul. In this sweat lodge, there was much focus on the Montauk Wellness Center and bringing it into being.

One of the results was that Sandra Sabatini created Sacred Spirit Tours to help facilitate this purpose. She was surprised, however, to see how vehemently she would be attacked for her participation, and it has been a very rugged journey for her which she has somehow pleasantly survived. It has thus occurred to me that some explanations are in order with regard to these matters.

Since *The Montauk Project: Experiments in Time* was released in 1992, it captured the imagination of thousands and there have been all sorts of people who have wanted to help or get involved in some way. Most of these people went by the wayside over a decade ago. There have been others who have tried to capitalize on the information and use it to their own advantage or for their own glorification. These efforts have, for the most part, been lame or insignificant. Others have been completely repelled by the very idea that there was a Montauk Project. The reason for this intense fascination and repulsion coupled with an ineptness to do anything about it has to do with the very mechanics or what is at play with regard to Montauk.

Montauk is a witness to or represents the very keystone by which the coherent system we call a universe is held together. The project described by Preston Nichols was monkeying with factors that not only changed the way people think but how this thinking ties into the fabric of how things are held together. Time was manipulated and chaos ensued. The power of this attracts people and understandably excites the imagination. Underlying all of this is the sacred energy of the very spot they used (Camp Hero) which was once under the guardianship of the Pharoahs of antiquity as represented by the Montauks and their ancient heritage. The Pharoah stood as the interlocutor and filter between the heavens and the Earth. You see a remnant of this stewardship in the legacy of the White House as a majority of U.S. presidents share the bloodline of the Montauks.

Putting the Montauk Pharoahs back on the map is like arranging a transfer of power from the leader of the Illuminati, the Bilderbergers or even the Vatican except for one thing. The office of the Pharoah of Montauk and what it represents is more powerful than all of those groups put together. Just look at all of the scholars and authors who have tried to make their mark with regard to Egypt. As I have been learning, such scholars do not even know where the Egyptian language originated from. What is far worse, however, are the politicians and secret societies which try to squeeze every ounce of power they can from Egyptian symbolism as well as the region itself. Montauk, and I am not exaggerating, is far bigger in its implications.

It is through Montauk that certain Bulgarians contacted me to teach us a clearer view of the Pharaonic civilizations as well as history itself. It is also through my work with Montauk that I was brought into the fold, as reported in *Transylvanian Sunrise*, about the chambers beneath sphinx in both Romania and Egypt. This is another point that various would-be prophets have sought to discover for their own prestige and glorification. It is no accident that these discoveries have and will come to the attention of most of the world via the Montauk research and story line. It is therefore no accident that David was making his first public presentation of the time chamber at Montauk.

His lecture was a streamlined and more user-friendly version of what I witnessed in Romania the previous year. He deleted the mathematical complexities. Most of what he said can be found on his website at *www.andersoninstitute.com* if you have the time and patience to read it. The most special part, however, was that he showed a video of the time-warp chamber.

Inside the time-warp field, an amaryllis plant was placed that was revealed as a small, tightly-closed bud. Horticulturists projected a four-day window for it to bloom fully. During this video presentation, it bloomed in under three minutes. David also mentioned that they were able to "reverse" its stage of blooming – to regress it back almost into a bud again – however, the field became unstable at one late point in the regression and it was exposed to high-level gamma rays which destroyed the plant life. This was not shown at this presentation. They have long since remedied the unstable boundary field.

It should also be mentioned that there was a professional photographer in attendance whom I know, and he commented that what we saw could not possibly have been "time-lapse" photography due to the saturation of colors that was displayed in the video. Keep in mind that this particular video is several generations behind the more advanced work that has been going on in recent years. As David has said many times, the Government is always ten to fifteen years ahead of what it informs the public about.

This was obviously a breathtaking event. David also indulged the audience by taking all of their questions afterwards. This was a very rare opportunity for people to Q&A with David, and it all came courtesy of the Medicine Man's return to Montauk and his dream for a wellness center. This last point should not be underestimated. The chances of the Medicine Man and David Anderson coming to Montauk by themselves were not good at all. That they should show up at the same time during a presentation of time control technology is all the more significant. That the incident occurred in sequence with both a sweat lodge and the REM state of dreams should also be noted.

David was set to leave the morning after his presentation, but we had breakfast and got a chance to talk privately. This was the breakfast meeting I had dreamed about although it was in a very different location. It is noteworthy to add here that I was absolutely right about the last name of the character in my dream who said he knew David. To my surprise, it turns out this man actually works at the Anderson Institute and is involved in the time experiments. David even told me I was right about the man's nickname which had been divulged in the dream. This confirms what I said about my connection to David and his work through the REM realm of the sleep state. There have been other experiences as well.

Despite these amazing revelations, I was still very curious as to why David had requested a face to face meeting with me. It was actually quite simple. He wanted to talk about my participation at Atlantykron that summer and what I wanted to do or present. As we talked, I mentioned a fledgling and ad hoc film project I had participated in the previous year that was cut short due to unfortunate circumstances. I then suggested that we produce a film/video with the students and remove the obstacles that prevented last year's fiasco which was never formally organized. David loved the idea, and the result was some rather remarkable synchronicity that continued the sacred journey that I thought I had left behind in Transylvania.

5

TRANSYLVANIA

As I mused over my ability to "pick up" on one of Dr. Anderson's employees through the REM realm of the dream state, I recalled a dream I had experienced over twenty years earlier that was obviously working its way into the interesting scenario I was now involved in.

Years before I became a published author, I wrote a short story based upon a dream I had. In the dream, I was sneaking into Dracula's castle based upon the Bela Lugosi movie. At the end, it is sunrise and I was reaching to Dracula so as to apprehend him as he tried to escape. I reached for his cape as the sun rose, and Dracula eluded my grip by turning into a white bat after which he changed back into human form but his clothing and cape were now white instead of the traditional black. In this "white" form, he said that he was the antithesis of his evil personification in the movies. I wrote this as a short story but it was long forgotten until Tantra Bensko, who accompanied me on my first trip to Romania, asked me if I had any fiction that she could include in an upcoming lucid fiction anthology. I told her about that story and read it to her over the phone. She liked it very much.

The theme in this rather detailed and unusual dream got some more life as soon as I returned from my Montauk adventure with David Anderson where he showed us the video of his time control chamber. Just four days prior to the Montauk seminar, I had received a copy of an email dialogue between Tantra and a friend of hers named Eve Logren, a well known therapist who wrote the book *Love Bites* about alien love bites. This email caught my attention because it was talking about a Transylvania Colony that was proposed as the 14th Colony of the Americas. I had never heard of it but was curious if it had anything to do with Transylvania in Europe. When I returned from Montauk, I did my own research and learned the following common history about the so called Transylvania Colony.

In 1775, a judge of dubious reputation by the name of Richard Henderson formed the Transylvania Company with the intention of making the Transylvania Purchase, a huge tract of land that made up what is mostly the modern state of Kentucky. American frontiersman, Daniel Boone, was hired to trailblaze the Cumberland Gap so as to access this land. Boone was also involved in the final negotiations to purchase this land from the Cherokees. The purchase was problematic because there were other Indians who claimed the land and Boone lost some family members over this. The purchase was eventually voided because the legislatures of both Virginia and North Carolina claimed parts of the land citing an edict by King George III which stated that colonists could not purchase land from Indians.

After reading these curious facts about the Transylvania Purchase, a couple of interesting thoughts occurred to me. First, King George III is well known for his insanity (see the book *The Madness of King George* by Alan Bennett) that revolved around his struggle with porphyria, a disease that is also known as "blue-blood's disease," one of the symptoms of which is purple urine, also referred to as "purple rain." It is well known that the first historical case of this disease is from his ancestor, Mary Queen of Scots, whose lineage traces back to Transylvania. Porphyria is also associated with Rh negative blood. The second thing that occurred to me is that one of the most documented cases of Rh negative[*] "blue people" is in Kentucky. You can read about the Blue Fugates of Kentucky (on the internet) for further information.

[*] I have written extensively about Rh negative blue bloods in *The Black Sun* and *The Montauk Book of the Living*. This includes members of the blue race like Machandi.

I wondered if the area where these Blue Fugates were from was the same part of Kentucky that was part of the Transylvania Purchase. Sure enough, I found out that the Blue People of Kentucky were located right in the heart of what was once referred to as the Transylvania Purchase. I also learned on the internet that a native by the name of Blue Otter stated that, according to his people, there was an ancient race of Blue People who lived underground. It should be noted that Kentucky is studded with some of the most extensive and beautiful caves in the world. They were so special that Aleister Crowley himself made mention of these caves in his autobiography and went out of his way to visit them when he was in America.

While contemplating these facts, I learned there was another extreme element of synchronicity at play. I knew that Sandra Sabatini of Sacred Spirit Tours, who had been with us at Montauk where she got to meet David Anderson for the first time, was from Kentucky. When I called her to tell her about all of this, she informed me that she was moving back to Kentucky that week. When I questioned her about the above information, I learned that her father's land was right in the middle of this "Blue People Country" although she knew nothing about this until I informed her. She soon found that there were artifacts on her father's property of an ancient civilization and that some rogue archeologists had been removing them. I also contacted my friend Mary Sutherland who told me a mouthful.

Mary has a whole thread on the Blue People of Kentucky on her website and she has also visited the area. There is even a picture of her with a very large pre-Columbian statue of a Caucasian head who is referred to as the "Serpent Prince" and is recognized as either Sumerian or pre-Sumerian. She has said that there are a multitude of artifacts in plain sight but that only the locals know where they are and they are not that friendly with outsiders. She subsequently introduced me to Rick Osman by teleconference who is preparing an extensive video documentary on the pre-Columbian settlements of Prince Madoc. He has witnessed all of these settlements which were all erected on older fortifications which are plainly in sight and which in turn were erected on previous fortifications from even more ancient times. This is hidden history and will be coming forth soon.

All of this is fascinating in and of itself, but it still does not explain how the name Transylvania came into play in American history. Despite extensive searches, I have found no logical etymology and only a few admitted speculations. Transylvania is most often said to mean "across the woods" or "beyond the woods." The Hungarians, who originally occupied Transylvania, called it *Erdély* which was derived from *Erdő-elve*, meaning "beyond the forest"). *Erdő* means "mountain deep forest" with the *elve* suffix being a derivative of the older form *elü* (meaning beyond). What I would point out in all of this is how *elve* quite apparently transmogrified into the English word *elf*.

In any event, there is great magic in this equation and Sandy Sabatini's connection to this area was indicating that synchronicity was the guiding principle. I had taken a sacred journey to the heart of Transylvania in Europe and was now receiving a deeper meaning to the word itself but also discovering mysterious threads that tied mysteriously into ancient history which also concerns the Blue Race of which Machandi is a part. Just as my travel to Transylvania with Nicole had been overshadowed via synchronicity by my association with David Anderson, so had this thread of investigation been prompted by his appearance at Montauk where he showed us a video of his time control chamber.

Continuing to investigate the mysterious thread between Kentucky and Romania, I looked to see if there was any common denominator between Transylvania in Kentucky and that in Europe. This led to a rather astonishing discovery and that is St. Germain (Rákóczi is his real family name), the famous Prince of Transylvania who, according to Manly P. Hall's *Secret Destiny of America*, was present in America during the settlement of the Transylvania Colony and also instigated the Declaration of Independence as well as the revolution itself. Hall also asserts that

St. Germain was a reincarnation of Francis Bacon, the author of *The New Atlantis* (as well as Shakespeare's plays) which positions America as the New Atlantis. Bacon and St. Germain were both Rosicrucians.

As Benjamin Franklin is also deeply tied to the Rosicrucians, I looked for a connection there and found out that he was a major investor in the Transylvania Company as were many politically influential colonists such as George Washington, Alexander Hamilton, and possibly Thomas Jefferson. Franklin and Jefferson both travelled to Paris where St. Germain also resided according to regular history. His presence in Paris is tied to the French Revolution. The common denominator in all of this is Rosicrucianism, a powerful secret society. Freemasonry and the Illuminati lurk in the background as well, and it is a well known fact that Jefferson commented on and corresponded with Adam Weishaupt, the founder of the Bavarian Illuminati. In such a scenario, it is anyone's guess what "illuminated" agendas were at work.

When we consider the realm of quantum synchronicity, which is obviously the principle at work, we are forced to consider that there is a quantum affinity (to use a term from quantum physics) or magical sympathy (to use a term from magick) at work here. The historical references and conclusions about St. Germain, to say nothing of the idealized New Age notions about him, state that he was tantamount to a time traveler. Not only did he appear in too many places at too many different times, he also cavorted with royalty and those in positions of political power. While I do not for a minute mean to suggest that David Anderson is St. Germain, there is a resonance here because David knows political leaders and also lives behind a veil of mystery. The legends of St. Germain, not the historical facts, also state that he had access to underground facilities and laboratories that are somewhat similar to those described in *Transylvanian Sunrise*.

When we consider the REM realm of sleep, it is important to note that David is the one who brought me to Romania in the first place and instigated these mysteries. The "magic" of synchronicity was demonstrated again with Nicole when we took our sacred journey to Sarmizegetusa on the very ten year anniversary of my initial meeting with David Anderson which had occurred on the same day the foundation stone was laid for the monastery we stayed in. I reiterate the REM realm factor of sleep because, well before I heard about the Montauk Project or became involved in writing the story, I had my dream about Dracula turning into a white bat. It was as if the dream state was pulling me to Transylvania long before my writing career would pull me there. Machandi also works through dreams as stated in Radu's story.

A year before I took the sacred journey with Nicole, however, there was another remarkable REM experience that came from Sandy Sabatini. She shared a dream with me where she was in a chamber with David Anderson and myself. Her description of this chamber was such that it made me think she had read *Transylvanian Sunrise* which features such a chamber. This was surprising because the book had not even been released at that point in time and there was no way she could have read it. In some strange way, she was picking up on what was in the book.

In Sandy's dream, the importance of the 24th chromosome was stressed, particularly as it relates to a coming planetary shift. Further, she recognized David Anderson in what was termed "The Great Mystery." She insisted that I relay this message to David before I go to Romania, but I was not too keen on this as I knew he would not understand or likely respond. I did send it, but he did not respond. He eventually did respond to an email of Sandy's, however, and indicated he would like to talk to her.

Sandy's dream included that David has artifacts that somehow, when activated by a DNA/key that includes "a method sequence," could protect the planet. In *Transylvanian Sunrise*, Cezar Brad originally accessed the chamber when his DNA was recognized at a security check point that was built millennia ago. This is how a force field was lifted that enabled final access. It is not known if it was Cezar's individual DNA or hand print that was recognized or just his general type of DNA. I assume but do not know that it was his individual DNA as if he was appointed in time to open this remarkable door.

Sandy's dream correspondence is amazing, and she had more to say without knowledge of the material in the book. She said that the three of us are being brought together for the coming planetary shift to stop something. When we consider the prospect of protecting the planet, it should be pointed out that the chamber beneath the Sphinx gave a holographic read out on how the entire geography and ecosystem of Romania was either protected or could be protected by the mechanism within the mountain. It was as if the technology for protecting that area of the earth was all figured out long ago. There is no reason that this protection mechanism does not also extend to Egypt, Tibet, Baghdad, Mongolia and the other underground areas that are mentioned in the book. Sandy said that there are seven locations in this regard that could protect the planet and one is in New Mexico. At that time, she did not know that David had a time control research center in New Mexico. While we cannot fully analyze the REM realm statements at this time, they were intuitive at the very least.

With regard to the "24th chromosome," let us next consider the chamber mentioned in *Transylvanian Sunrise* which includes the ability to read out one's DNA in holographic format down to the molecular and atomic constituents. It can also go beyond that, but Radu Cinamar did not have time to explore this in the first book. What is also not mentioned is the potential for the technology to read out the circumstances of the 23rd gene-pair. We do know that the technology can perform holographic read-outs of potential hybridization between alien life forms. The 23rd gene-pair, however, represents a different aspect than mere hybridization.

There are 23 gene-pairs in human DNA. Each gene-pair consists of two chromosomes that are linked together. Although there are 46 chromosomes in human DNA which make up 23 gene-pairs (of chromosomes), people find it easier and more expressive to simply refer to this 23rd gene-pair as the 23rd chromosome which is not only the sex chromosome but a "magical" chromosome. This part of the equation is not science fiction.

There is also much New Age hoopla generated about the prospects of the so-called 23rd chromosome which includes the "awakening" of the Galactic Center which will emit a cosmic ray which will change all of our DNA and transform the human race. This is part wishful thinking based upon some science, legends and creative thinking.

Above and beyond the New Age hype, there is biological evidence indicating that there was once a 23rd and 24th gene-pair that fused into what we now call the 23rd gene-pair. Two gene-pairs became one gene-pair. This was an a priori state to what we now recognize as an ordinary human being. Al Bielek has long said that this "23rd chromosome" was deliberately altered at some point in the history of the human race.

When I told a friend of mine about this, she knew exactly what I was talking about and said that Preston Nichols should find the frequency that will "uncollapse" these two gene-pairs. Bringing it up to Preston, he then informed me that he has been working on it, but it is an extremely complex series of frequencies. It is not a simple solution.

What I would like to point out is that when chromosomes combine with each other in ordinary biological functions, it results in disease. I am referring to the chromosomes of one gene combining with that of another. Most diseases, including hereditary disease, are the result of an admixture of chromosomes which is another way to express the idea of a "collapse." It therefore becomes apparent that if the 23rd sex "chromosome" is really the result of two collapsed or fused gene-pairs, then this affliction is representative of a master disease in the human body that is shared by virtually all humans. It is also a disease which is "hard-wired" into the genetic structure of the body and is not expected to change or dissipate easily. Keep in mind that the word *disease* is a compound of *dis* and *ease*. Even if you are functioning normally in ordinary human terms, your lungs and brain are not operating anywhere near full capacity.

The implications of these facts are staggering if one chooses to extrapolate. It suggests that the shape-shifting abilities of shamans and other paranormal attributes might be functional if humans possessed a 23rd and 24th gene-pair that was not collapsed. This prospect places us into the realm of occult biology, at least as far as academic science on this planet is concerned.

With regard to Sandy's prophetic dream, it suggests that my work with David Anderson is centered around the transformation of the human race on a very profound level. The elements included are: David Anderson's time control technology, the chamber beneath the Sphinx and all the technology inside, the mysterious 23rd gene-pair, and Cezar Brad's adventures into the Inner Earth. We can now also add in Radu's adventures with Elinor, Repa Sundhi and Machandi which most certainly are concerned with transforming the human race.

Sandy's dream also included a blue pharaoh who had a language written on his face. The dream indicated that the pharaoh represents a bloodline that is part of the circle I am gathering around me to activate such. This special DNA suggests the Merovignian bloodline which is very often misunderstood by modern writers. Merovignian represents the Vine of the Moors which includes the Montauk Indians who are the Royal Pharoahs. The language on the face of the blue pharoah is supposed to represent a key to activating artifacts that include a form of time travel. A person, through their DNA, has to know how to activate it. This is Sandy's dream talking, not me.

In such a manner, the REM realm of sleep and scientific theories are swirling around the prospects presented in the book *Transylvanian Sunrise* that are also synchronizing with the theme of time travel as well as the Montauk Pharoahs. The blue pharoah in Sandy's dream is not only in keeping with Machandi's blue color but also the blue people I have written about in previous books such as *The Black Sun* and *The Montauk Book of the Living*.

Sandy also had an odd occurrence in the early to mid 1990s when she received a mysterious letter from a Dr. David Anderson of the Time Travel Research Center. As far as anyone knows, David's time operations were not public at that time. Sandy only came to know him through her association with me. When we were at Montauk, she asked David about it and he only smiled as if to say that such strange phenomena is sometimes part of his work with time. He did not own up to remembering having sent the letter, but he did not deny it either.

If we consider the people I am gathering around me, it is important to note the following thread of facts that have developed throughout the last twenty years. They tell their own story.

In 1990, I came across the most unique and bizarre amalgamation of science, technology and occultism imaginable through the personage of Preston Nichols. It is all centered around the most elusive and mysterious phenomena in science: time. As I helped Preston write *The Montauk Project*, a lot of phenomena and strange experiences were generated which were based upon synchronicity, a manifestation of time.

Following the path of synchronicity led me to the discovery of the Pharoahs of Montauk and the actual historical legacy of an ancient Blue Race of people that settled in the Inner Earth and set up the ancient cultures of Atlantis, Egypt, Tibet and India. It should be noted that the name *Krishna* means "dark blue."

One of the most bizarre synchronicities I encountered concerns the mysterious Anderson family of Montauk legend who were the guardians of time. Although this was not a key story line, it was one of the first things I learned about with regard to the legends of Montauk. The entrance of Dr. David Anderson and his time control technology into my life therefore took on extra significance. David also arranged for me to travel to Romania where my sacred journey to the ancient spiritual capital of Transylvania is inextricably tied to my association with him.

My connection to Radu occurred only after *The Montauk Project: Experiments in Time* was translated into the Romanian language and literally enabled Daksha Publishing to be created. Radu Cinamar saw the book and submitted his manuscript for *Transylvanian Sunrise* to the publisher. The manuscript was then translated into English, sent to Sky Books and eventually published. Radu and I thus became associated.

Another important aspect to this story line occurred when a descendant of the Montauk Pharoahs, Artie "Red Medicine" Crippen, came into my life. As a youth, he was approached by two Lakota medicine men who travelled across the country to see him because their tribe had been waiting 30,000 years for him to incarnate. He is the only one to properly complete their gruelling Sun Dance ritual. Artie, an adept practitioner of the martial arts, introduced me to his instructor, Roosevelt Gainey, the founder of the Taoist System of Living Arts.

I have written about Roosevelt Gainey at length in *The Montauk Book of the Living*, but he is by far the most advanced being I have met in a human body. Without recapitulating all that I have already written about him, he understands the functionality of the human body in ways that are beyond the comprehension of modern institutionalized science. This applies to both healing and martial arts. I have studied with him consistently for almost four years at this writing. When I told him about the yidam in this book, he knew exactly what I was talking about and began talking about how this applies to seven different levels of energy. This is something I am going to be learning more about, but it also shows there is a continuation of and more meat to the story line than anyone might have imagined.

How and why people gather together has a lot to do with the principle of quantum affinity: like attracts like. The chamber beneath the Romanian Sphinx presents many interesting aspects in this regard, particularly with regard to DNA and the holographic readouts. This comes into focus when we consider a somewhat obscure book entitled *The I Ching and The Genetic Code: The Hidden Key to Life* by Dr. Martin Schönberger which has also been expounded upon and diagramed on the internet. It reveals that there is a correlation between the *I Ching* and the way our human biology is expressed through DNA.

DNA, it should be remembered, is the interface between life and matter. When spirit mobilizes matter and animates it, it does so through the mechanism of DNA and thereby combines into the plethora of life forms on this planet. The correlation with the *I Ching* is important because it is based upon yin and yang as expressed in a broken line and an unbroken line. This is the same thing as a binary digit in a computer code. Each molecule of DNA consists of codons which are information units which store all sorts of different data. Codons can be virtually represented either as binary digits or the broken and unbroken lines of the *I Ching* which then form into various patterns of combined lines or digits which symbolize all of the various permutations of dynamic functions that manifest in life experience, including biological manifestations.

As putting together the various patterns of yin-yang lines will demonstrate, polarized opposites attract and repel in such a manner as to produce a self-propagating unit which combines with other units to form various biological units which in turn propagate. Underlying this is the quantum principle of resonance or "like attracts like." In other words, this principle of quantum mechanisms visibly demonstrates itself to be the underlying principle of our biological framework. Once again, each molecule of DNA consists of codons which are information units which store all sorts of different data. The biological building blocks all correlate with the principle of synchronicity. Like attracts like in order to form into organisms.

A very important point in the aforementioned book by Dr. Schönberger is that DNA is not just a stand-alone molecule. It also has a wave character (according to F.A. Popp) which implies that there is a universal system of communication between the cells of the body which operate at far higher speeds than the humoral or neural systems and at velocities ranging between the speed of sound and light. In such a manner, ultraviolet biosignals ride along the spirals and activate specific codons (information). This amounts to a synchronicity of information.

It also tells us that the paranormal abilities of a Chi Gong master are facilitated when the biosystem of his body is operating at a very high speed which includes a rather intense synchronicity of movement. There is a law in Taoist Chi Gong that applies here and it has to do with what is called "melting."

Taoist Chi Gong has many aspects to it, but there are nine laws which are an important foundation. They consist of how to move your physical body or respond to another. The ninth law is: "To put it all together, Melt." This is the most elusive of the nine laws because you are putting together everything you have learned into one synchronized movement. You might say that when a professional athlete, sports team or a group of musicians "put it all together" in a startling performance, they are melting by calling on all of their pro experience. Melting, however, bridges into a new set of laws which are energetic and perceptual in nature as opposed to physical. To completely Melt, one would employ all of the energetic laws, too. Beyond the energetic laws, there are mental laws and beyond those are spiritual laws wherein one becomes familiar with the mysterious vapors.

This level of Chi Gong I have just mentioned is very advanced. I brought it up, however, because it ties in with the creation of the yidam who, as Repa Sundhi stated, is created from the mental plane of an advanced adept. It gives another reference frame by which to appreciate Radu's adventures. To tell you the truth, most of my Chi Gong practice concerns itself with the physical aspects. This is the level where one begins. I do, however, have my moments of advanced perceptions. The more I engage in it, the greater the adventure.

There is also a lucid dreaming aspect to Chi Gong that ties into these experiences. Machandi uses the dream state as do I. Between the two of us, we have both utilized the dream state to meet half-way through the very book you are reading. While she works from a loftier plane, I work from the earth plane.

There is much more to what I am saying here, but most human beings are not even up to learning and practicing the physical laws of Chi Gong which require exercise and hard work. Most people, if interested in improving themselves at all, are content to listen to the gurus on television who are not really clued in at all. They have some knowledge, but it is akin to an academic professor who knows how to read and write but misses the truths uttered in this book about space-time physics or archeology. The discipline I am talking about is not available in New Age road shows or even decent establishments that provide reasonably good services.

I have also mentioned the idea of Melting because it represents the macrocosmic aspect of what is going on in my work, particularly as it relates to Sandy's aforementioned dream with regard to the gathering of characters around me. It is as if the stage is being set for a Grand Melting of planetary proportions. While I cannot prove this to you, this is what my experiences are indicating. It is, quite obviously, an intuitive process with plenty of linear tangents. Linear tangents are very important if not the most important aspect in all of my work, and I always attempt to stress this aspect.

If you have read this far in the book, you probably have the idea that there is some truth behind what Radu has mentioned in his writings. I would like to corroborate this by adding an observation with regard to what happened to Radu. When he had his second encounter with Machandi, there is very little that occurs by way of a verbal description. It was very obvious to me, however, that Machandi took him into a state which I recognize from Taoist Chi Gong as the "Great Stillness." This is a very profound state of spirituality. It became obvious to me that she is a Taoist master in her own right and would have to have a tremendous familiarity with the aforesaid laws of Taoist Chi Gong, particularly for her to reach Radu in the way that she did. It is a very rare experience for such an enlightened being to jump start someone's consciousness in such a faction.

Thus it is that an extremely interesting if not a very strong case has been made for Radu's story being true. The holographic computers that read out the DNA of different life forms are a significant and delightful mystery. With those capabilities, there is no reason not to believe that they could not also solve the problem of the mysterious 24th gene-pair or at least give detailed explanations that would solve it. The chamber beneath the sphinx also contained a vessel with a special form of monatomic white gold. In my past work, this subject was expounded upon as was its role with regard to the Blue Race and the full awakening of consciousness in a human being. It would therefore be reasonable to assume that the computer facility in the Bucegi Mountains was either erected by the Blue Race or a life form closely associated with them. When we consider that the binary aspects of DNA fit hand-in-hand with computer technology, it stands to reason that the underlying principle of quantum mechanics in biology would resonate with the master technology available in the chamber. Like attracts like. In such a manner, it is not really so odd that the themes I have written on and explored are now manifesting before us in a tangible scenario that deeply touches the entire planet.

What I have presented above is the promise or hope of a remarkable solution that could potentially be available to all life forms on this planet. As exists in any good drama, however, there is opposition to such hopes and dreams. Since my last meeting with David Anderson, his life has been threatened and he has not been able to release his videos demonstrating the more spectacular aspects of his own time research. Although he oversaw my list trip to Atlantykron in Romania, he did not venture there himself. It was a security issue.

Radu has been warned by his superiors that he is not to write anything further for the time being. Suffice it to say there are forces that want to maintain their own political control to the detriment of humanity at large. This, of course, is not a new situation on planet Earth.

What is interesting is that both Radu's adventures in this book and my own were centered in and around sacred locations in Transylvania. The theme of the Blue Race via Machandi has also converged upon Transylvania.

When I researched and released *The Black Sun* in 1997, it created a rather profound reaction. Besides containing pictures of some of the first Nazi flying saucer craft to appear in an American book, it explored Nazi occultism in a manner that had not been done previously, going beyond *The Morning of the Magicians* which deserves significant credit as the first popular book to reveal the Nazi occult connection. *The Black Sun* created a lot of controversy, but an entire line of books has since come out on these subjects by many different authors. Even mainstream Nazi authors were forced to embrace the data. *The Black Sun*, however, was not just about Nazis. It was also about Tibet, the Blue Race and monatomic gold. While the Tibetan issues have been mostly ignored, the monatomic gold theme had already been circulated in New Age circles but it was done so as to exploit gullible people who lacked proper discernment. Generally, most New Age and conspiracy readers are prone to hucksters.

The Black Sun did something unique in that it connected and correlated the white gold to the Blue Race and the Rh negative factor. The reaction to that data by Freemasonry was to have mind control victims seemingly spring up out of nowhere and spout all sorts of information about Rh negative being connected to shape-shifting reptilians. Different people picked up on this theme and exploited it, but it was all based upon information from people who had suffered traumatic mind control. It effectively muddied up the entire subject and polarized people against finding out the full circumstances and history with regard to the Blue Race. The term *goddess* is generally used in a pejorative sense by such mind control victims as are different esoteric and occult terms, the purpose being to discredit occultism in general. In other words, the subliminal message is to reject occult or hidden information.

The proposition put before us by Radu Cinamar and his accounts of Elinor, Repa Sundhi, and Machandi are designed to elevate humanity, a species which has demonstrated an inbred tendency to be suspicious of and resist any attempts to seriously increase its consciousness. This is why the planet suffers and the solutions that are implemented are only half-hearted. The core needs to be fixed, not just the obvious environmental issues that are mostly ignored. As Repa Sundhi has clearly stated, the planet is in a very critical state.

It is interesting that Repa Sundhi has also stated that he has high level connections in politics. Not only did he set up Department Zero for the Romanian government, he escaped Tibet as it was invaded and ended up working for the Chinese government. He has similar associations in many other countries, too. As I read Radu's book for the fourth time, these prospects caused me to rethink how David Anderson fits into these matters.

I have already written about the puzzling factors with regard to David thinking he had met Radu who has no recognition of such a meeting. As David also has associations at the highest levels of world leadership, it spurred the thought that Repa Sundhi might be a much more logical association for him. It also explains how he said he knew about Radu when I first asked him but not want to discuss it on the phone. I have asked David if he knows Repa Sundhi but have not received a response at this point. David often travels to the Far East, including China, but even if he does not know Repa Sundhi personally, I do know that he has mysterious partners that are tied to governments. It is highly likely that the more positive partners in time control technology might be allied to Repa Sundhi or put in place by him in the first place. Keep in mind that Repa Sundhi was able to activate a space-time portal. If the story is true, Repa Sundhi would likely be a senior consultant to David Anderson.

All of this makes for a delightful mystery. More importantly, it demonstrates that there is considerable effort being made on behalf of the planet by entities that are living outside of the

normal or average human paradigm. If the planet is going to seriously and drastically improve on a wide basis, it is obvious that
the human paradigm is going to have to change as well. Radu
and I are both hoping that this book can serve as a catalyst.

With regard to David, his role in my life has always been
rather mysterious. He was obviously attracted to my writing
ability and he has stated such. From the very beginning of
our association, however, he was also intent on bringing me to
Romania which he believes has a crucial role to play in the future with regard to east-west relations. In this regard, it reminds
me of the way Cezar approached Radu. He wanted him to write
a book. As time developed, however, he had much more in store
for Radu and so did Repa Sundhi and Machandi.

As things stand now, more mystery and adventures awaits.
The next step is for me to receive, read, and publish the transla-
tion of Radu's third book which is entitled *Misterul din Egipt:
Primul Tunel* which translates as *The Mystery of Egypt — The
First Tunnel*. If life moves as I would like it to, I hope to have it
ready early in 2012.

In *The Mystery of Egypt — First Tunnel*, Elinor leaves Romania for his own security reasons and proceeds to an unknown
destination. Before that happens, Radu is clued-in on Elinor's
villa in Bucharest which has a secret alchemical lab in the basement. Radu becomes the caretaker of this property and is particularly interested in the impressive library there.

After taking possession of the villa, Radu is unexpectedly
contacted by Cezar and taken to Alpha Base. Dr. Xien is wanted
by the secret service for occult reasons that have to do with inside government connections, but he is nowhere to be found. It
is hoped that Radu can reestablish this lost connection due to his
relationship with Machandi. It is a lost cause, however, at least
for the time being.

Radu then describes changes occurring inside the secret
military base in the Bucegi mountains and the particulars of the
tunnel in the Projection Room that leads to Egypt. He becomes

part of a five man team that was assembled to explore this tunnel. A fascinating account of this expedition is given accompanied by simple sketches. Cezar, who is also a part of the five man team, supplies Radu with a considerable amount of esoteric information. This includes an amazing account from 10,000 B.C. which he learned about in the Projection Hall but was not allowed to reveal until now.

The five man party also included a computer genius from the Pentagon, Romanian Lieutenant Nicoara of Department Zero, and a Special Service Lieutenant who ends up being unveiled as a USAP* (Unacknowledged Special Access Project) agent of the Secret Freemason World Government.

This party reaches the end of the tunnel without incident and an occult chamber is discovered. It is accurately described in minute detail and includes the following: an immense library full of tables which is the obvious product of extraterrestrial technology and contains a "history" of our own galaxy and the universe; an antigravity gliding device; and a virtual replica of the enormous machine found in the Projection Hall that is adapted for human use. Cezar describes the latter as a time travel machine that allows the consciousness of the subject to be projected in an ever existing time dimension and gives full details of the true nature of time and of the akashic records. He also speaks of his time travel experiences.

Towards the end of Volume III, Radu describes his attempts to make use of the time machine. After two consecutive failures, he obtains a quick projection into a secret tunnel of the Great Pyramid of Cheops. Radu suddenly realizes that the scientific community does not have a clue about it when he is confronted with the vision of the real masters of the pyramids from long forgotten times.

The fourth book in the series is *Pergamentul Secret: Cinci Tehnici Initiatice Tibetane* which translates into English as

---

* In *Transylvania Sunrise*, it was incorrectly stated that USAP referred to the United States Antarctic Program instead of Unacknowledged Special Access Project.

Secret Parchment: Five Tibetan Initiation Techniques. If things go according to plans, my translator will complete this shortly after finishing the third book. *Secret Parchment* is a translation of the manuscript Radu was given by Machandi. The book also contains information about the reorganization of Department Zero and their liaison with the United States Government. Radu visits a top secret installation in Maryland which includes interaction with the remote viewing community. Since Cezar left to become an ambassador to the Inner Earth, the political pressure to suppress Radu's books had increased. As I write this, it has increased to an unprecedented extent. Riots have broken out in Egypt which are politically tied to access of the chambers discussed in *The Mystery of Egypt.*

It looks like both book three and book four will be released in 2012 with *Secret Parchment* being released just as the Mayan calendar comes to an end. I personally have no beliefs or commitments attached to this date. Preston's Montauk research was more concerned with 2013.

My intuition tells me that I will finally meet Radu when his first four books have been published in English. I think we will then write a fifth book, either together or separately.

In summary, my dream of over twenty years ago appears to have pulled me to the heart of Transylvania and paved the way for all of these remarkable adventures. The ancient history of Transylvania, however, goes far beyond whatever you, I or academe has ever considered. I learned more about this when I travelled to Bulgaria after my 2010 visit to Romania. In Bulgaria, I was greeted by my Bulgarian publisher who took me on a whirlwind tour of the ancient ruins of his country. It was a ten day trip which is too long to go into here. I took over ten hours of video footage and hope to release that at some point in the future. What I will share at this point is rather brief, but serious historians in Bulgaria (not necessarily the academics) know that ancient culture emanated from the proto-Thracian culture that was centered around Bulgaria but also embraced the area we now know as Romania. There are lots of stone chambers and even reports of more exotic high tech chambers as well.

What I want to stress here is what Radu said about the events in the *Ramayana* having occurred in Transylvania. The *Ramayana* is one of the two great classics of Vedic or Indian literature, the other being the *Bhagavad Gita*. The *Ramayana* is about the blue god Rama and his wife Sita. It is briefly discussed in Radu's narrative, but I would encourage all readers to read outside sources for a better understanding, keeping in mind that it is only a surface history. The *Bhagavad Gita* is concerned with the blue god Krishna whose very name means dark blue. This obviously applies to the Blue Race and an ancient history that is long lost to historians.

I am bringing this up because it ties in to one of the biggest targets of oppression in Eastern Europe and also applies to the rest of Europe as well. I am referring to the Gypsies, who are known as the Roma. The names Roma and Rama are intimately tied to one another phonetically and etymologically. There is a scholarly etymology which demonstrates that the word *Roma* derived from *Rama*. Students of phonetics will realize that vowels are interchangeable anyway. This revelation becomes very important with regard to the Roma because there origins are obscure. There namesake and culture are very much tied to Romania but their Hindi-like appearance and language have convinced many that they originated in India.

A thorough study of Bulgarian history will teach you that the Vedic, Egyptian, Persian and Chinese cultures emanated from Eastern Europe. There was also an ancient priest-king of the proto-Thracian Bulgarian culture who was known as Sham and this is where the word shaman originated. The third letter of the Bulgarian alphabet is *vede* and this is where the Vedic culture gets its name. Lao Tzu's ancestry was from Bulgaria as were the techniques he brought with him. The Egyptian cat goddess Bast was buried in her native country and has a tomb on the border of Bulgaria and Turkey which is recognized as her tomb in ancient Tibetan scrolls. More details of this are for a different day, but my point here is that this explains how the Roma and their Romani language could have derived from Rama in Transylvania, migrated to India and returned, if it ever fully left in the first place. There are many common or similar words that *Roma* and *Romanian* share. It should also be pointed out that scholars indicate that Romanian derived from Latin when soldiers from Rome retired in Romania. This has been demonstrated as faulty as the Romanian language is closer in structure to Classical Latin than it is to Vulgar Latin which was the vernacular at the time the Roman soldiers invaded and eventually lived in Romania. Why would the Romanians develop a language that is similar to a language that was no longer spoken? Misconceptions yield to obvious facts.

The word *rama*[*] means "dark" in Sanskrit so it is referring to either "dark blue" as in the word *krishna* or just "darkness." Rama was identified as a blue god in literature. So it is that our journey becomes circular, feeding back on itself like a closed time-like curve. The more we study time, the more we learn about ancient history and vice versa.

I will look forward to Radu's next installment and hope that you too can read it soon.

---

[*] The phoneme *ra* can also be construed as "cat" when you consider that the Chief of the Erie Mound Builders has taught me that *ir* means cat as in Erie or Iroquois. *Ra* is the same as *ira* when the *i* is dropped. The *ma* in *Rama* can also be construed as cat when you consider that *mau* and *mao* both mean cat in Egyptian and Chinese. Not only is Rama construable as "two cats" but his wife, Sita, also has a name that means cat. My friend, Sid Catlett, has taught me this etymology which he learned through a very hard lesson. Both of his names mean cat. Sid derives from *cit* which became *city* which is based upon a fairy mound called a *sidhe* which is a portal to another world. Cities were often built around such a magical site. The word *site* comes from *sidhe*. If you consider that the word *Moor* also means cat, you have a deeper understanding of the foundations at work here. The Roma, like the Moors, have been suppressed for centuries because they represent the feminine. The secret name of Roma, Italy (Rome is Roma in Italian) is *Amor* (*Roma* reversed), a word which means "love" and also refers to *Moor*. Signor Massini, his people, and the Vatican all represent the antithesis of the Moors.

APPENDIX A

Most of our experiences in the physical universe conform to Newtonian laws and/or what is referred to as Galilean relativity. Galileo determined that there exists an absolute space in which Newton's laws are true and that there is a universal time and space. Among other things, Einstein's Special Theory of Relativity expands this theory but also takes different observers into account (like those experiencing time dilation while travelling near the speed of light) and states that the speed of light is the same for all inertial observers regardless of the state of motion of the source.

A very important corollary of Einstein's Special Theory of Relativity, and in particular with regard to the work and breakthroughs of Dr. David Anderson, is something known as the Invariance of the Space-Time Interval. The understanding of the Space-Time Interval is critical to creatively apply time-warped field theory that is the cornerstone of the reactor designs being operated today by Dr. Anderson. The term Space-Time Interval simply refers to the space or time separation between any two events in the universe. The interval or measurement between two events is really a very simple proposition and will yield to simple arithmetical or geometrical calculation without any difficulty unless we consider different observers observing from different vantage points. Of particular note in this could be an observer in a space ship travelling near the speed of light. As time will dilate for him, he might travel from point A to point B and back in a shorter time (from his perspective as well as the measurement of the watch he had on his arm) than someone observing it from a space station between the two points.

Einstein's Theory of Special Relativity, as well as other physicists who have made further proofs of this, tell us that no matter where the observer is or in what mode he is travelling, the Space-Time Interval between the two points will always be the same. This is known as the Invariance of the Space-Time Interval. If this sounds simple, it should. It is common sense, but scientists have also subjected this to excruciating proof to account for time dilation and other phenomena associated with near-speed-of-light phenomena. So, in summary, the Invariance of the Space-Time Interval refers to the fact that no matter the motion status of the observer, the time and distance between two points or two events in space will always be the same.

There is an equation, based upon the work and postulates of Einstein, that scientists use for figuring out the Space-Time Interval. It is based upon the Pythagorean Theorem which is $a^2 + b^2 = c^2$. (The sum of the square of two sides of a right triangle will equal the square of the hypotenuse). As the equation of the Space-Time Interval is a bit more complicated, I will first present the rationale with regard as to how it fits into the Pythagorean Theorem. This will give you a very important foundation to understanding time that is not clear from reading most ordinary or advanced physics books.

To demonstrate his theory, Einstein postulated a traveler (think of a rocket or spaceship moving near light speed) as having a clock that was based upon a beam of light flashing between two mirrors arbitrarily placed at three feet apart for easy computational purposes. The beam of light, moving at c (the speed of light which is virtually the same as the speed of one foot per nanosecond), is going to tick (digitally or otherwise) once every three nanoseconds.

Now, both you and a rocket traveller have identical clocks, but you are at a stationary point such as a space station or at home base. As the rocket man moves at near the speed of light so will his mirror be moving at such a speed. As your clock emanates a beam from Mirror #1, it moves straight in the direction of your second mirror (Mirror #2 as per the previous example). His clock, however, (if you were to be able to see it — see example below) would be emanating a beam of light from his Mirror #1 that would hit a location different than the original location of where his second mirror (Mirror #2) once was. Four nanoseconds later, his Mirror #2 would be four feet to the right when the

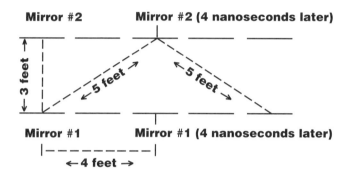

beams reaches it. The beam will then zigzag down and up, etc. as the rocket ship zooms through space.

One can therefore easily see that if the mirror had travelled four feet during this period, one has a right triangle situation where the Pythagorean Theorem applies and the hypotenuse is now deduced to be five feet. This example is included so you can appreciate how the Pythagorean Theorem is utilized in a scientific equation known as the Invariance of the Space-Time Interval which is as follows:

$$\left(\text{Spacetime} \right)^2 = \left(C \times \left\{ \begin{array}{c} \text{time} \\ \text{separation} \end{array} \right\} \right)^2 - \left(\begin{array}{c} \text{space} \\ \text{separation} \end{array} \right)^2$$

This equation is standard science recognized by physicists universally. You can see how it fits in with the Pythagorean Theorem when we extrapolate by saying that if $a^2 + b^2 = c^2$ then it is also true that $a^2 = c^2 - b^2$. Note that as the astronaut in the rocket and his mirror clock move, he is experiencing time dilation. In other words, he

(Equation reproduced from last page for convenient reference)

$$\left(\begin{array}{c}\text{Spacetime}\\ \text{Interval}\end{array}\right)^2 = \left(C \times \left\{\begin{array}{c}\text{time}\\ \text{separation}\\ \text{seconds}\end{array}\right\}\right)^2 - \left(\begin{array}{c}\text{space}\\ \text{separation}\\ \text{meters}\end{array}\right)^2$$

will age slower than you or whoever is in the space station when he returns after travelling at near light speed.

What is new, and what Dr. David Anderson brings to the table, is that the measurement of the astronaut can be conveyed in terms of **distance**. The astronaut is moving through space but his mirror can be clocked in terms of distance by reason of the mirror example. The hypotenuse of the right triangle represents the velocity of a light beam with reference to the speed of light or a fraction of the speed of light, depending upon how fast the

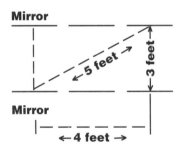

beam is moving. Further, the speed of light itself can be expressed in distance as light moves 3×10^8 feet per second. **Time can be referenced to distance. This is a very important point.** Why? It gives a common unit of measurement between time and space which is otherwise unknown to modern physics. Further, the application of this principle can be applied when looking under a high powered microscope, to lasers, or any other technology you can imagine. One can navigate their way through any coordinate system of any kind. Time is now less mysterious as a concept but also to technological applications as well.

APPENDIX B

As part of his time travel studies, Dr. David Anderson recognized that the earth, or any rotating body such as a planet, coexists with what is termed "twisted spacetime." This is not a new concept to science. Einstein's theory of general relativity predicted that rotating bodies drag space-time around themselves in a phenomenon known as frame-dragging. In what amounts to a rough metaphor, imagine the air swirling around a tornado that displaces dust and air that moves around it. So does the actual fabric of space-time move when a planet rotates, but it does so very slightly.

The rotational frame-dragging effect was first figured out from the theory of general relativity in 1918 by Austrian physicists Josef Lense and Hans Thirring who predicted that the rotation of an object would alter space and time, thus dragging a nearby object out of position in contrast to the prediction of Newtonian physics. This effect, however is infinitesimal and amounts to one part in a few trillion and requires a very sensitive instrument to measure it.

Although this twisting of spacetime is very small, a huge rotating body like the earth contains enormous levels of potential energy by reason of the tension in the fabric of spacetime that is caused by inertial frame-dragging. These observations have led Dr. Anderson to formulate a system which will harvest and apply the stored potential energy between points separated by regions of twisted or curved spacetime or hyperspace. It is called a time reactor and there is a patent pending on it.

The implications of these theories and their accompanying patent by Dr. Anderson are staggering because it completely changes the paradigm with regard to power generation. This system is clean and inexpensive compared to current systems in use and there are no dangerous by-products. A time reactor not only generates high levels of clean power but also containable and controllable time-warped fields and closed time-like curves and is able to utilize the stored potential energy across any region of curved spacetime or hyperspace. This includes any area of curved spacetime, whether naturally or artificially created. A time reactor is the only system of its kind that will generate such power and time-warped fields.

There is no limit to the size of a time reactor. It could be a micro device or a power station that harnesses the frame dragging aspects of the earth itself. There are infinite applications and ones that I have not touched upon yet, but we will first briefly address some technical aspects.

The system components of a time reactor include the following: 1) The Environment; 2) The Reactor Emitter; 3) The Reactor Power Collector; 4) The Energy Storage Device; 5) The Power Conduit; 6) The Reactor Control System and 7) The Reactor Field Chamber. A brief description of each follows.

1) The Environment is any region between and including two or more separated points in between which is a region of man-made or naturally-occurring curved spacetime or hyperspace.

2) The Reactor Emitter is an assembly located at any of a set of multiple points in space that are separated across a region of curved spacetime or hyperspace which produces an information and energy beam when activated. The form of the beam may include but is not limited to thermal, chemical, electrical, radiant, nuclear, magnetic, elastic, sound, mechanical, spacetime-generated or any other form of information and energy known in the art that has the ability to enable the coupling and discharge of the spacetime-motive force stored within regions of curved spacetime or hyperspace.

3) The Reactor Power Collector is an assembly located at any of a set of multiple points that are separated across a region of curved spacetime or hyperspace which captures the energy within the spacetime-motive force when it is coupled and discharged between the points.

4) The Energy Storage Device is an assembly that receives, stores, and releases energy created by the operation of the time reactor. The forms of the energy stored, processed and released by the energy storage device may include but are not limited to thermal, chemical, electrical, radiant, nuclear, magnetic, elastic, sound, mechanical and spacetime-generated energy. The energy storage device may consist of other types of energy storage devices known in the art, including but not limited to batteries and fuel cells.

5) The Power Conduit comprises an energy conducting pathway connecting a reactor power collector to the energy storage device. It may be of any material or structure known in the art with the ability to conduct forms of energy including but not limited to thermal, chemical, electrical, radiant, nuclear, magnetic, elastic, sound, mechanical and spacetime-generated energy.

6) The Reactor Control System comprises feedback, monitoring and control of all parts, components, and operation of the time reactor. This includes all devices and communications necessary to sense, manage, command, direct or regulate the behavior of all time reactor parts and components. Devices may include but are not limited to, sensors, controllers, actuators, computer systems, communications, software algorithms and the operator human-machine interfaces needed to successfully operate the time reactor.

7) The Reactor Field Chamber is an assembly with a volumetric area located near a reactor power collector and the energy storage device of the time reactor. The reactor field chamber is positioned near and within the effects of fields generated by the operation of the time reactor. The reactor field chamber creates an environment for monitoring, study, experimentation, and application of the fields generated by operation of the time reactor. This applies to many types of fields dependent on the type of energy being accessed, channeled or generated by operation of the reactor. This includes the fields generated by spacetime-motive forces within the reactor field chamber that includes but is not

limited to time-warped fields, fields of closed time-like curves, and any fields producing variations of special spacetime geometries.

A basic time reactor may include just one emitter and collector or arrays of each. There is no limit to different configurations that might be employed. Further, the form of the energy captured is unlimited and may vary and the invention is not limited to power generation but can even be used for more exotic applications such as time acceleration and deceleration within the reactor field chamber. This is accomplished when the fields generated by the coupling of spacetime-motive force are concentrated and controlled in or near the reactor field chamber in order to produce time-warped fields. Such fields include closed time-like curves which allow for the time acceleration and deceleration. Once again, there are multiple applications.

Other exotic applications of a time reactor include the creation of carrier waveforms in the structure of spacetime that may permit modulation and accelerated long distance communication through spacetime or hyperspace. It may also be possible to use the characteristics of the coupled spacetime motive force and the time reactor to create fields providing force-at-a-distance through spacetime. This is akin to force fields you have seen on Star Trek or in other science fiction stories. In addition, the invention creates conditions that may be valuable for multidimensional computing and many applications in research and development in the area of spacetime physics and high-energy systems.

Does all of this sound too incredible to be true? It should, but it is actually being patented in the United States Patent Office. This is not a theory but an application that has actually been subject to laboratory experiments.

This not only solves the world's energy problems, it suggests there will be wide-sweeping changes that put us on the precipice of a space opera society. These wonderful technological breakthroughs mentioned here, however, are only as good as they can be implemented. You all know the stories of how

Tesla's miraculous inventions were shelved by the power elite. We next have to consider the politics of change with regard to implementing this technology.

David has long said that all technology which is released to the public, whether it be laptops, cell phones or any other gadget, is in government hands at least 15 or 20 years before it is released to the public. This suggests that such time control has been familiar to them and that they are only now allowing him to release it.

For more information and updates, please refer to Dr. David Anderson's website *www.andersoninstitute.com*.

APPENDIX C

In the original version of *Transylvanian Sunrise*, there were different sketches of the Projection Hall beneath the Romanian Sphinx in the Bucegi Mountains. For some reason, three of these diagrams were omitted and are now included herewith.

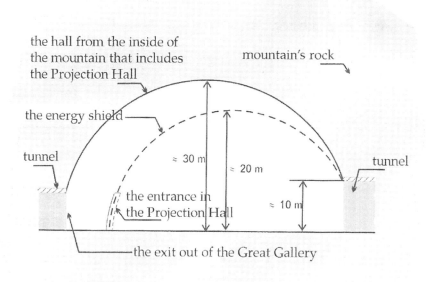

TRANSVERSAL SECTION OF HALL INSIDE MOUNTAIN WHICH INCLUDES PROJECTION HALL

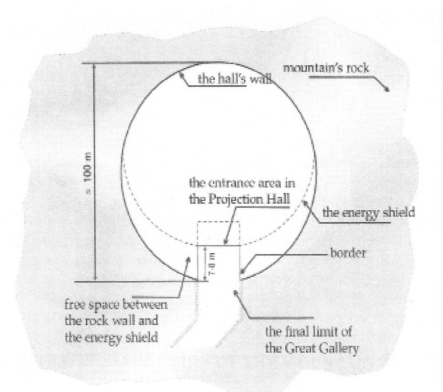

the hall's wall

mountain's rock

the entrance area in
the Projection Hall

the energy shield

≈ 100 m

7-8 m

border

free space between
the rock wall and
the energy shield

the final limit of
the Great Gallery

**VIEW FROM THE TOP
OF THE MOUNTAIN ROOM**

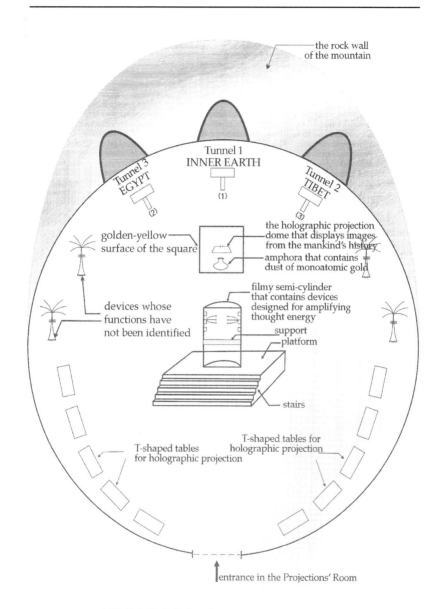

the rock wall
of the mountain

Tunnel 1
INNER EARTH
(1)

Tunnel 3
EGYPT
(2)

Tunnel 2
TIBET
(3)

golden-yellow
surface of the square

the holographic projection
dome that displays images
from the mankind's history

amphora that contains
dust of monoatomic gold

filmy semi-cylinder
that contains devices
designed for amplifying
thought energy

devices whose
functions have
not been identified

support
platform

stairs

T-shaped tables for
holographic projection

T-shaped tables
for holographic projection

entrance in the Projections' Room

INTERIOR HALL OF THE PROJECTION HALL ROOM

SAGE ADVICE

It is an excellent idea to reread this book multiple times. With each reading, you will see, understand and realize things you did not quite fathom before. The same advice applies to this book's predecessor, *Transylvanian Sunrise*.

read this book in ebook format...

Sky Books is converting all of its publications to ebook format

The Montauk Project, Transylvanian Sunrise and *Transylvanian Moonrise* are now available in ebook format as of May 2011. Our other publications should all be available in ebook format by the year 2012 or earlier.

Check on amazon.com or other ebook outlets for further information and updates or email us at:

skybooks@yahoo.com

TRANSYLVANIA BLOGGING

If you would like to comment or interact with others with regard to the mysteries and events taking place in Romania, please visit our blog. This is an opportunity to network and for everyone to learn and contribute to the unfolding story. This will be a live and interactive forum and if we are lucky, we might get some contributions from Radu Cinamar or even others involved in the scenario described in *Transylvania Moonrise*. Subjects will include the Montauk Project, time travel, and the lastest developments of David Anderson. Please come and join us at *www.digitalmontauk.com*.

WWW.DIGITALMONTAUK.COM

THE MONTAUK PULSE

Those who would like to receive updates on Peter Moon's adventures with David Anderson and the ground-breaking events that are occurring in Romania should subscribe to the Montauk Pulse newsletter. The Montauk Pulse originally went into print in the winter of 1993 to chronicle the events and discoveries regarding the ongoing investigation of the Montauk Project by Preston Nichols and Peter Moon. It has remained in print and been issued quarterly ever since. With a minimum of six pages and a distinct identity of its own, the Pulse has expanded to not only chronicle the developments concerning the Montauk investigation, but has expanded to include all the adventures that have surrounded Peter Moon since that time. This includes his association with the Montauk Tribe and the Medicine Man of the Montauks. Subscribing to The Pulse directly contributes to the efforts of the authors in writing more books and chronicling the effort to understand time and all of its components. Past support has been crucial to what has developed thus far. We appreciate your support in helping to unravel various mysteries of Earth-based and non-Earth-based consciousness. It makes a difference.

To subscribe to the Montauk Pulse, please send $20.00 (includes shipping). If you are outside the USA add $12.00 shipping/handling charges to: Sky Books, Box 769, Westbury, NY 11590-0104

HOPEMART

As part of his work with the World Genesis Foundation, David Anderson has contracted with major corporations, including Walmart, to establish **www.hopemart.org**, a website that is not only dedicated to providing a pleasant and relatively inexpensive shopping experience but one where a sizable portion of each sale will go to the World Genesis Foundation. Donations from said corporations are expected to range from ten to fifteen percent in most cases. If you are an internet shopper or would like to start shopping on the internet, you can participate in this program by going to **www.hopemart.org**. Every purchase makes a difference in a young child's life.

Sky Books   **ORDER FORM**

We wait for ALL checks to clear before shipping. This includes Priority Mail orders. If you want to speed delivery time, please send a U.S. Money Order or use MasterCard or Visa. Those orders will be shipped right away.
Complete this order form and send with payment or credit card information to:
Sky Books, Box 769, Westbury, New York 11590-0104

Name	
Address	
City	
State / Country	Zip
Daytime Phone (In case we have a question) ( )	

☐ This is my first order   ☐ I have ordered before   ☐ This is a new address

Method of Payment: ☐ Visa   ☐ MasterCard   ☐ Money Order   ☐ Check

\# _____ — _____ — _____

Expiration Date   Signature

Title	Qty	Price
The Montauk Pulse (1 year - no shipping for US orders).....$20.00		
Subtotal		
For delivery in NY add 8.625% tax		
Shipping: see chart on the next page		
U.S. only: Priority Mail		
Total		

Thank you for your order. We appreciate your business.

For a complimentary listing of
special interdimensional books and videos —
send a $1.39 stamp or one dollar to:
Sky Books, Box 769, Westbury, NY 11590-0104

FUTURE BOOKS

&

OTHER TITLES

Please visit our website:
www.skybooksusa.com or www.digitalmontauk.com